GULF
LANDSCAPES

**by Elizabeth Collas
and Andrew Taylor**

*Published with
the support and
encouragement of
Gulf Landscape Services*

Published by
Motivate Publishing

PO Box 2331
Dubai, UAE
Tel: 246060
Fax: 245270

PO Box 43072
Abu Dhabi, UAE
Tel: 311666
Fax: 311888

London House
26/40, Kensington High Street
London W8 4PF
Tel: 071 937 4024
Fax: 071 937 7293

Directors:
Obaid Humaid Al Tayer
Ian Fairservice

Senior Editor:
Julia Roles

First published 1992

ISBN 1 873544 34 0

Printed by Al-Ghurair Printing &
Publishing House

CONTENTS

Cover: Viewing the landscape from Fossil Rock. (Photo: Peter Roles)
This page: Dune contours. (Photo: Jonathan Ali Khan)

Storm clouds over Fossil Valley.

INTRODUCTION

From out of a clear blue sky, the storm clouds gathered over the mountains of Oman in a matter of minutes. As the light faded, so did the sharp black shadows that gave the rock faces their crumpled, twisted appearance, and the whole mountain chain became dark, lowering, and threatening. It was an ominous silhouette, against a heavy blue sky.

A minute or two later came the wind, whipping up the sand and gravel and flinging it into our faces. And within half-an-hour it was all over: the sun was shining again in a sky of picture-postcard blue, and the mountains were shot through once more with brown and red and orange where the different rocks caught the sunlight.

But a little distance down the road, the way was blocked: rains further up in the mountains were cascading down the bare rock, and flooding over the wadi (valley). A few people sounded their horns impatiently, as if they expected the noise to part the tumbling waters; the wiser ones knew they simply had to wait.

It was a moment's insight into the sudden changes in the weather of the Arabian Peninsula, and into the way that the whole landscape slowly forms and changes itself, with the movement of the sand and gravel, the sudden shock of the water and the constant, steady glare of the sun.

And if there was a single moment that made us interested in trying to work out how and why the landscape was like it is, that was it.

In one chapter, we try to explain something of the incredible story about how the Hajar Mountains were formed hundreds of kilometres away, pushed slowly across the sea, and finally heaved up on top of the Arabian Peninsula.

But amazing as that story is, it's the simpler, more obvious changes in the landscape that we found irresistible. Because there is so little vegetation here, and because the rocky slopes are usually not disguised by soil, it's easy to see the fold lines and the strata of the different rocks. The whole machinery of the formation of a mountain landscape practically unfolds in front of you.

The same factors of wind, water and sun, with the occasional upheaval of the entire land-mass from deep below the earth, have created coastline, deserts and mountains alike. And the beauty of it is, it's all so clear to see.

DESERT SANDS

It is a different sun that sets among the sand dunes.

It's altogether bigger, and a deeper, heavier red. It sinks quickly in the sky: there is little twilight.

All the guide books tell you never to venture into the desert without a second car for company, and certainly never alone. It's good advice; yet observing it means missing one of the great experiences of the Gulf.

Because the only way to watch the sun set in the desert is on your own.

Perhaps a good compromise is to park your four-wheel-drive on the slope of a dune, then go on up on foot, leaving your companions behind in their cars. On the other side of the ridge, if you've chosen the dune well, you'll be able to sit in solitude and watch the sun go down.

Even if you've only walked a few metres, you will gain some tiny impression of how vast and lonely the sands can be.

For a few minutes, as the sun hangs low above the horizon, the dunes are still, and the shadows that break them up, black and impenetrable. As those shadows lengthen, you'll see the delicate tracery of ripples patterned across the surface of the sand; they're a reminder that, for all the apparent stillness, the whole of Arabia is constantly on the move beneath you.

The infinitely slow movement of the massive plates of rock that make up the earth's crust means that the entire peninsula is edging towards the north-east with the ticking of the geological clock. But on top of that irresistibly shifting base, the sands of the desert are constantly forming and re-forming into dunes, sometimes a hundred metres high or more. The dunes themselves move steadily across the landscape, and

In the sands near Fossil Rock.

7

on their surface, the lightest of breezes leaves its traces in the tiny parallel waves in the sand.

The study of the specialist is to know more and more about less and less — and that's as true in physical geography as anywhere else. Just observing the way these tiny ripples are formed is material for dozens of theses and books.

In a way, they demonstrate how the massive dunes of Liwa and the Empty Quarter were formed before them, with the slightest breeze picking up individual grains of sand and piling them up until they resulted in a stable mass two or three centimetres high.

That ripple provides shelter for the few centimetres of sand beyond it, and so another ripple forms a little distance away. And another. And another. The ripples of sand on the dunes are a shifting map of the movement of the winds across the sand.

Dunes

In fact, anything that's dry enough to blow around, whether it's snow, dust, or sand, will form drifts. Sometimes it's easy to see why — as, for example, when sand is blown up and around a hill or a rocky outcrop, or even around an old oil drum or a dead camel.

The winds may blow the sand right up against the obstruction, as they have against Fossil Rock, near Dhaid. Or, if they change direction, they may eddy around the obstruction, leaving a gap between it and the pile of sand.

Anything lying in the desert can start the formation of a sand dune, and once the pile of sand is there, it creates its own momentum. The grains of sand are blown up the windward slope, to fall down the steeper side beyond the crest, building up the dune all the time.

More often, though, the dunes simply seem to appear by themselves in the middle of what should be a vast plain of sand.

If you go back to the billions of individual grains, it's easier to understand. They're blown along by the wind, bouncing over hard, stony ground, until they come to a softer patch of sand. On that, they don't bounce so high, so they don't travel so fast. That means there's more sand arriving on the wind than there is being blown away: and so the dune begins to build up.

Ripples in the dunes: a shifting map of the movement of the winds across the sand.

It develops its own stability as its lee side grows steeper and steeper, until it reaches the point at which fresh dry sand simply rolls down it. As Wilfred Thesiger discovered, it's a stability that is very easily disturbed. He wrote about what can happen, in *Arabian Sands* :

"While we were leading our camels down a steep dune face, I was suddenly conscious of a low vibrant hum, which grew in volume until it sounded as though an aeroplane were flying low over our heads. The camels plunged about, tugging at their head ropes, and looking back at the slope above us. The sound ceased as we reached the bottom. This was the singing of the sands."

The singing sands

Thesiger's feet, and those of his camels, had disturbed the delicate equilibrium of the slope, and a whole layer of sand was slipping down towards the bottom, making the eerie noise as it rubbed against the layer below.

It was a phenomenon that St John Philby had already experienced. In *The Empty Quarter*, written 27 years before Thesiger's book, he describes how he even tried to catch the singing sands in a glass bottle. He didn't succeed.

"I threw myself into a kneeling position on the singing mass, into which my knees penetrated to a depth of 12 inches or so. I then thrust my bottle deep into the singing sand, and as I drew it out, noticed a remarkable suctional sound, as of a trombone.

"It also seemed to me that there was a hollowness deep below the surface, but it would probably be difficult to be certain of that...."

It would indeed. For all their diversity, one feature shared by dunes is that they are resolutely solid — sand all the way through.

The only trombones that play are those in the minds of people who hear the singing sands — and none the less magnificent for that. But it's an experience we've never had: and it's easy to be dismissive about things you've never heard or seen.

In any case, the way that dunes are formed from the flat desert sands, and then moved imperceptibly across the landscape, seems impressive enough in its own right.

The annual shamal wind which blows from the north-west, hated for the dust-storms it brings with it, is probably the biggest single influence on creating and moving dunes across the whole Arabian Peninsula.

Rocky outcrops can change the shape of the dunes by sheltering them from the wind.

Camels on the dunes near Shwaib.

The grit in the air as the shamal blows is nothing less than the deserts on the move. The crystalline rocks of the Hajar Mountains, broken down over the centuries, washed down into the wadis, and winnowed out by the wind; the coastal sands from around the Gulf; the dust as rocky outcrops such as Jebel Hafit are slowly worn away by wind and weather — the dunes of the desert are a visible sign of the ageing of the whole peninsula.

It's a miracle that you can actually feel and see in the making.

Even so, out of the Arabian Peninsula's million square kilometres of sand, there are vast tracts where the desert stretches out, flat and featureless, as far as the eye can see — areas, for instance, around the vast sand-sea of the Rub Al Khali, the Empty Quarter.

The same winds blow across these 'sand sheets' as elsewhere in the region. So why are there no sand dunes?

In some areas, it's because the rudimentary vegetation holds the sand together so well that the dunes have no chance to form. Elsewhere, it's the result of occasional floods forming a hard, impermeable crust on top of the sand.

Plants hold the shifting sands together near Umm Al Quwain.

Grit in the air — a shamal screams through the desert.

Wind direction

Across the arid Empty Quarter, though, the explanation is generally simpler: it's the coarse sand that was too heavy for the winds blowing into the desert. This is the sand that the centuries left behind — the remnant not even good enough for sand dunes, which lies flat and heavy, almost like fine gravel.

But the dunes that do form in the softer sand are much more than random piles heaped up by the wind. Depending on how much sand there is to blow about, how big the individual grains are, and how steadily the winds blow from one direction, different types of dune will form across the landscape.

The strength of the wind, interestingly enough, has nothing to do with the type of sand dunes that are formed. It's entirely a question of the sand, and the wind's direction.

Near the coast, for example, the winds almost always blow in off the sea, and so the dunes have established themselves along the line of those prevailing winds. Further inland, where the winds shift about more, the sand is built up across the line of the prevailing wind; and where there is less loose sand to blow around, horseshoe-shaped dunes known as barchans may form themselves into intricate, interlocking patterns as the winds shift direction.

The more the winds change, the more complex the patterns of the dunes will become. In the middle of Arabia's vast sand-seas, for instance, where there is no limit to the amount of sand to be blown around by the constantly shifting winds, star-shaped dunes grow, with the sand collecting in the middle of long, swirling fingers of sand. The lighter and finer the sand is, the more distinct will be its shape, with a long gentle slope towards the prevailing wind, a steeper scarp slope on the lee side, and a sharp ridge dividing the two.

Fine sand

Where the sand is really finely ground, that ridge can look razor sharp as it cuts across the desert. Coarser sand, though, will fight back, forming either low, ill-defined dunes across the line of the prevailing wind, or rounded hummocks of sand where the winds have changed direction as the dune was forming. It almost seems as though the unwilling sand has been forced grudgingly into shape.

But it's never as simple as that. The student who has studied the drawings of the different types of sand dunes in his textbooks will be as disappointed in the deserts of Arabia as the layman will be amazed. The dunes on the ground are more complex than the pictures in the books.

In any area, a hundred different factors will be at work, with new systems of sand dunes building up on top of the old ones.

The dunes themselves, once established, may channel the winds one way or another; each gust from each direction will have its own complicating effect on the final pattern. The prevailing wind is never the only one to blow.

The most fascinating individual dunes, of course, are the magnificently curved barchans, bigger versions of the ones to be seen near Sharjah Airport. Often, they're linked together, in almost symmetrical patterns: sometimes, single barchans jut defiantly out, curving round to protect the tiny area of shelter between their two arms as they move slowly across the landscape before the wind.

Most dunes move, although some of the massive ones of the Rub Al Khali, the Empty Quarter, are believed to have stood in the same place for thousands of years — but it's the barchans which march steadily across the desert before the wind. The long, curved arms, carrying less sand as they slope down towards their ends, are blown faster

Razor-edged dunes near Hatta.

Curvaceous dunes in the Liwa.

Plants in the dunes near the Hatta road: their roots hold the sand together, making it more stable.

than the middle of the dune, so they curl around until they are in the shelter of the main body of sand as the whole dune inches forward.

Barchans are found mainly on the edges of the sand-seas, where the sand is in shorter supply. Further in come the long straight dunes, either across the wind or parallel to it: they pass the grains of sand from end to end of the dune.

And then in the middle come the star-shaped dunes, gathering the sand together. While the movement of the continent is inexorable and steady, the sands on top of it are shifting in thousands of different directions at once.

For a people who relied on camels and an inherited sense of direction to move painstakingly around the desert, that presented its own problems. Wilfred Thesiger, in *Arabian Sands*, described a small taste of the discomfort of desert travelling in a sandstorm:

"We sat throughout the day, without shelter, in a reddish obscurity, half smothered by the flying grains which, reaching to a height of about eight feet above the ground, rasped our skins, filled our eyes, noses, and ears, and were gritty between our teeth."

It's a description that may seem familiar when the shamal blows, even to today's traveller in his air-conditioned four-wheel-drive vehicle.

For the bedu, though, sudden sandstorms could wipe out tracks and landmarks, leaving even experienced travellers lost and helpless in the desert. The difficulties for a modern society

Desert scrub near Fossil Rock.

Trekking through the desert: camels near Falaj Al Mualla.

with roads and fixed routes are less drastic, but just as intractable.

In Qatar, it's common to see the way simply diverted around a sand dune that has drifted across the old road — a sort of fatalistic acceptance of *force majeure*.

Elsewhere — along the road from Dubai to Al Ain, for instance — lines of ghaf trees have been planted along the windward side of the road to break up the winds and prevent the dunes from forming. In other places, workmen have covered the sand with pebbles or sprayed it with oil to make it less susceptible to the wind.

None of it works for ever. Had he had the transport available, King Canute could have taught his courtiers the same lesson in the sands of Arabia as they learned on the banks of the Thames.

Arabian lights

But it's not just the sands themselves that move: for many people, watching the sands for the first time, it's the delicately shifting colours in the desert light that are so memorable.

Near Al Ain, for instance, just off the Abu Dhabi Road, lies a magnificent series of dunes up to 50 metres high, tinged with the red glow of iron oxide in the sand. With the changing light, the dunes will shift gently from a pale rose colour to orange, ochre, carmine, russet, umber and, as the sun finally goes down, to a rich deep purple.

Iron ore deposits in the sands may give a heavy red sheen to the landscape; and nearer the coast, ground down remnants of seashells, and lingering salt deposits which leave the sand dead and infertile, may give the dunes a whitish, dusty appearance.

Dying dunes

But anyone who believes that sand dunes have no life of their own simply isn't looking. We travelled early one morning out towards Hatta, searching for barchans and instead, found a whole pattern of living and dead dunes spread out on the plain below us.

We'd clambered up a rocky outcrop cursing ourselves for having brought neither camera nor, even more important, water on what had been planned as a brief foray before breakfast. What we saw seemed chaotic at first, without any system to it at all.

Running in serried ranks across the landscape were lines of old, dying dunes, rounded now along their crests, and gradually sinking back into the desert floor as the winds whipped the sand off them. Since they were formed, the prevailing winds had changed, and on top of them was a whole new system of small, sharp-crested ridges.

The desert was changing its shape almost before our eyes.

That's the life *of* the dunes: but we found the life *on* them, too, to be astonishing in its variety.

It's hard to believe as you gaze out over the parched, scrubby landscape, but the sand dunes hold their own reservoirs of water for plants with roots deep enough to reach them.

Usually, the moisture in the ground is sucked towards the surface by capillary action, to be evaporated by the sun. Sand, because it's such a bad conductor of the sun's heat, and because it's composed of big, distinct particles separated from each other by gaps of air, doesn't work like that.

The air gaps allow the water to sink straight through to the water-table beneath, instead of

Sand dunes hold their own reservoirs of water for plants with roots deep enough to reach them.

being trapped near the surface, as it would be by ordinary soil.

Partly because it's so deep, and partly because the sand insulates it from the heat of the sun, it's not drawn back towards the surface, and so most of the water which falls in the desert's infrequent but heavy rainstorms never evaporates.

Instead of vanishing into the air, it lies within the dunes, seeping out occasionally where a valley falls below the level of the water table, to form oases like those at Liwa — water where none should be.

Relying partly on that scanty supply, hardy, dried-up-looking plants and windswept bushes slowly colonise the sand, changing the shapes of the dunes themselves as they do so.

Many, like the arta bush which pushes its taproot deep into the desert sands, may seem to be dead and dry for much of the year, only to spring into life without warning. Others, such as the mesquite bush, can survive for long stretches on nothing but dew; still others have seeds that can lie dormant in the sand for months or even years.

There are the abal bushes, and the qassis on which travelling bedu used to rely for their camels' grazing.

Slowly, as the plants take hold, they will begin to make the sand more stable. Their roots will hold it together, and their leaves and branches trap blown sand in still more patterns.

And as they grow bigger, they begin to channel the winds around themselves, gradually changing the shape and structure of the sand dune on which they grow.

Some of the dune systems are impressive for their sheer size — particularly the massive red dunes at Liwa, some of them 200 metres high. Many people travel just to see them; others go to ski down them, or drive up and down them in four-wheel-drive vehicles.

The sheer fun of dune driving is immense: after screaming up the shallow slope as fast as you dare, there comes a moment when your vehicle rears up over the crest like a dinosaur lurching out of a primeval swamp. Everything in the windscreen suddenly turns to sky, and then suddenly you are on the downhill side, at an angle you never believed possible.

Hold your nerve, and keep pointing straight to the bottom, and you'll be all right — this is the moment these vehicles were built for.

A place for peace

It's thrilling and exhilarating, but we feel a bit uneasy about enjoying it so much, even though the tracks we've left in the dunes have been erased by the wind within hours. Sand and wind are, after all, endlessly renewable. But if dune driving became really popular, the damage that might be done to the plants and animals that scratch out a precarious living among the sands would be immense.

And there's also a feeling that it's somehow disrespectful to these huge, slowly shifting mountains of sand to roar all over them, spewing out exhaust fumes and engine noise.

Perhaps they really are best appreciated in tranquillity: maybe the desert is a place for peace rather than exhilaration.

Dune driving near Falaj Al Mualla.

WATER IN THE DESERT

It is the suddenness with which the desert springs to life that is so astonishing.

Whether it's the rolling red sands of Liwa, or the flat gravel plains that lead up to Dhaid, the landscape can change within a few hundred yards to produce a fertile area of grass, date palms, and crops. It is as though the desert, exhausted, were suddenly taking a breath.

It was the detailed knowledge of these occasional and unaccountable patches of green, as well as the smaller hidden wells and springs, that enabled the bedu to travel as they did, squeezing the last drops of water from the countryside as if from a sponge. News of changing watercourses, dry wells and hidden springs was passed from one to another as the most valuable commodity that could be exchanged. Modern travellers can only guess at the numbing relief with which the most hardened bedu must have greeted the oases as they suddenly appeared below the dunes.

And, just as the sea and the occasional fresh water from the wadis caused villages to spring up along the coast of the Emirates, so the oases tempted a few families to settle and survive on what they could grow. With the prosperity of oil, of course, those settlements developed a momentum of their own, and grew beyond recognition. However, because the water supply remained the same while the demands upon it grew, several are now beginning to exhaust the oasis on which they were founded.

Hatta, in fact, is not a true oasis: the water here comes from wells which have been sunk deep down to the underground water system, and from falajes (irrigation channels) carrying it from the nearby hills. The water supply at Dhaid,

Lush vegetation at Khatwa.

21

Falaj and date palms at Khatwa, near Buraimi.

on the edge of the outwash gravels, is much the same, with supplies seeping under the gravel base, ready to be trapped by wells.

At Hatta, though, there was enough water to establish the village as an important transit centre on the caravan route between Al Ain and Oman — a role which led to the building of watchtowers on several of the rocky outcrops, as the villagers established their defences against less well-intentioned travellers.

No-one knows for sure exactly what the source of Hatta's underground water supply is. When Hatta Fort Hotel was opened more than 10 years ago, the builders bored 17 artesian wells to keep it supplied, even though several of them gave only brackish and cloudy water. The deepest sank down nearly 200 metres into the ground.

It's believed that they are tapping into an underground river running along the surface of the impermeable rock base, and the sunken lagoon which it feeds — but the interest now is largely academic.

Growth of a town

The few buildings which once housed the people who tended the date palms, and those who supplied the travelling caravans, have grown in recent years to a town of some 6,500 people, many of them with their own experimental gardens and swimming pools. Often, they grow their own fruit and vegetables, and near the road towards Dubai, watermelon and other fruits are produced for sale.

It is a prodigal use of water that would have horrified the old inhabitants — and as a result, the water table has steadily sunk year by year, as the water is drained out of the hidden lagoon faster then the underground watercourses can replenish the supply.

Today, of the hotel's 17 wells, only three are ever used, and even for those, there is now a desalination plant to purify the brackish water that is often pumped up. The old water system cannot cope with the modern demands on it.

Over the last few years, the authorities have been installing a whole network of reservoirs to improve the supply. The original one, built in the mid-1980s, fills to a depth of 15 metres within an hour after heavy rain, as the water gushes down off the mountain side. Around it, another six reservoirs are linked together to trap as much water as possible.

But the community is still growing. Eventually, it's likely that water will have to be pumped out to Hatta from Jebel Ali's desalination plant: the oasis which brought the town into being will finally have been superseded.

The traditional water supply is dwindling at Al Ain as well, as the town grows, even though surveyors have found new natural supplies in the last few years. Once again, the water is hidden beneath the surface — though this time, the wells originally needed to go down only three or four metres.

As at Hatta, they were supplemented by falajes drawing supplies from the mountains, to support a small community of traders and farmers producing vegetables and tending a few animals.

For generations that was enough, but as demands grew, though, the water supply couldn't cope. More wells were dug in the 1960s, down to depths of 50 metres and more, as the population grew and as the oil money began to flood in to pay for the work. A new water supply was discovered far below the ground some 40 kilometres outside the town.

Hatta village is not a true oasis.

But in Al Ain too, the water table was retreating. Of 96 wells dug at the experimental Al Ain Wheat Project, for instance, more than a third have now dried up. At the same time, surveyors are constantly searching for new water courses and engineers have constructed a purification plant to enable recycled water to be used for watering the town's parks and gardens.

The effort to ease the pressure on the ancient water supply aimed firstly to develop additional water sources, and then to make the use of the water more efficient.

But, if it was ever a realistic aim to enable a town of 100,000 or more to survive on the original supplies, it failed. Water is pumped to Al Ain across the desert from Abu Dhabi: like Hatta, the town now has to rely on modern technology and the seawater of the Gulf.

It is at Liwa, though, that the best examples of a classic desert oasis are found. Beneath the dunes, some of them hundreds of feet high, the bedrock tilts gently from the south towards the north, bringing the water seeping gently downwards through the sand.

Al Ain — an oasis town.

In the heart of the dunes, capillary action sucks it towards the surface — but the movement is unlikely to be more than about a metre upwards every year, and the sand insulates the water from the fierce heat of the desert sun above. The result is that a reservoir of water, shaped like a gigantic lens, and following the contours of the dune, forms inside the sand.

To anyone who managed to dig down to it — a prodigious task, even without the sun on your back — it would appear merely to be an area of damp sand. But there is more than enough water stored between those sand grains to feed the oases on which the bedu used to rely.

In the hollows between the dunes, where the water-table is closer to the surface, enough water gathers to support date palms and vegetation. Pools form; this is the sort of oasis everyone imagines in the desert.

Usually, though, oases like this provide only a limited supply of water — enough to supply the occasional wandering group of nomads, but

not sufficient for a permanent settlement. And in the heart of the Empty Quarter, where there is virtually no rain, the dunes remain dry all the way through, and the hollows between them as arid as anywhere else. Water can move under the sands, as it does in the Liwa region — although no-one knows exactly where the source of that water supply is — but the oases are based on physics, not magic. If there is no rain, there can be no water, and if there's no water, there's no oasis.

Liwa is bigger and more extensive than most oasis systems. Here there is a whole series of similar oases in the different valleys between the dunes, each one of them supplied from a different 'lens' of water. They provide enough water to support the date plantations and enough vegetables for some of the landowners to truck into nearby towns for sale.

For the travelling bedu though, it would be the knowledge of the smaller, lesser-known waterholes that would save their lives in their wanderings through the desert — spots at which the water-table lay close enough to the surface to be reached by digging. Sometimes, the holes would have been covered by drifting sand, the only clue to their presence being the camel-dung around them.

Occasionally, wells several metres deep would have been dug. St John Philby describes one, about a metre square, almost buried at the foot of a steep sand-slope:

"The existing shaft is nine fathoms deep to water, the upper portion to a depth of some ten feet being cleared through loose sand and lined with a structure of wood and wattle to prevent it falling in. The remainder of the shaft is sunk through a reddish sandstone, and the water is brackish..."

As it often must have been. It's accounts like that which sketch in some of the harshness of the bedu's life.

Even today, the oases in the desert permit a slightly easier life for the people who live around them: only a generation or so ago though, they simply saved people from death.

Keeping the falajes flowing, to irrigate the plantations, demands constant work.

Palm trees at Liwa oasis.

THE MOUNTAINS

Two small children were carefully picking their way down the rock-strewn lower slopes of Jebel Huwayyah into Fossil Valley, clutching between them, like a shared trophy, a deep red stone about the size of half a brick. Etched on it, unmistakably, was the shape of a sea-shell some five centimetres across, with its parallel ridges clearly visible in the rock.

There is, of course, nothing unusual in a fossil, unless you are only five years old. The prized imprint the children were holding was simply a legacy of the days millions of years ago when Jebel Huwayyah was an underwater reef in a sea which stretched over practically all of the Arabian Peninsula.

Oysters, clams, and sea snails — or at least, their limestone death masks — can easily be found there scattered on the ground: it is the profusion of fossilised shells and tiny sea creatures that has given Fossil Valley its name. Millions of years ago, the limestone formed around their shells on the sea bottom, creating a natural mould which then filled with mineral salts and solidified, leaving a perfect replica of the long-dead creature.

Today, the rough horseshoe of hills which remains of the reef is an outcrop of the Hajar Mountains to the east — but in the days when the shellfish whose fossils now litter the ground were bathing in the salt water, the rocks of the Hajar were still being formed 2,000 kilometres away.

The geology of the whole region is rare, complex and fascinating. We look in more detail later as to why and how the level of the Gulf has risen and fallen over the centuries but as the sea has fallen back, it has left rocks like Jebel Huwayyah

Backbone of the Emirates: the Hajar Mountains.

The ruined summer palace at Wadi Hail.

The Awabi Fort in the Jebel Akhdar.

that were once underwater, high and dry and surrounded by desert. At the same time, massive upheavals have pushed the Hajar Mountains out of the sea bed and up on top of the Arabian landmass; and all the time, the whole continent has been implacably on the move.

Even after the hundreds of millions of years that have elapsed as the continent has formed and reformed itself, the evidence of how it happened and the way it used to be is still there to be seen.

Around Dubai and the Northern Emirates, and stretching far into Oman, the Hajar Mountains form a barren, bleak backdrop to the rich colours of the rolling desert scenery. The stony wadis that cut through them are like the bones of an animal, dried and baked clean by the blazing sun.

Forts and palaces

Within living memory, they provided a welcome haven for the wealthy who wanted to escape the non air-conditioned humidity and misery of summer on the coast. Just inland from Fujairah, for example, in a fold in the foothills, stand the ruins of the summer palace of Wadi Hail, where a little more altitude, a little more shade, and a little less humidity made the summer more bearable.

More sinister, though, is their history as a formidable redoubt for bandits and rebels. In the 1950s, faced with the combined forces of the Sultan and his British allies, Omani rebels withdrew into the Jebel Akhdar — a mountain retreat that had not been successfully stormed for nearly two thousand years.

It took a daring night-time assault by the Sultan's soldiers and the British Special Air Service to put the rebels to flight, and end both the rebellion and the Jebel Akhdar's reputation for impregnability.

Nowadays, drivers on metalled roads cross the mountain range with little more effort than a change of gear. Four-wheel-drives regularly pound up the wadi-beds on family picnic trips, raising clouds of dust behind them — but ten thousand years or so ago, practically yesterday in geological terms — regular rain meant the wadis were permanent tumbling rivers, dragging rocks and boulders down from the mountains to deposit them on the plains below.

In the years since then, winds carrying grains of sand have gradually smoothed the boulders down; iron, magnesium and clay minerals have been sweated out of them by the

The mountains of Oman look down on the Wahiba Sands, south of Muscat.

A formidable redoubt — fortifications in the Jebel Akhdar.

constant heat of the desert sun, giving the stones their black, polished appearance. It's a phenomenon well-known in areas of low rainfall, called 'desert varnish'. The hard, shiny coating formed by the stain can be up to a millimetre thick, and varies from red to black, depending on whether there is more iron or manganese in the rock.

In fact, it relies on some rainfall to dissolve the minerals inside the rock, leech them to the surface, and then leave them behind as a deposit when the sun evaporates the moisture. In desert and near-desert regions like this though, there is likely to be no subsequent rainfall to wash the deposits away: by the time the rains come again the desert varnish is set hard and permanent over the surface of the stone.

Near Fujairah, for instance, the covering of pebbles and gravel left by the rivers of centuries ago has created a black, glistening, stony plain between the shore and the mountains.

Those pebbles and boulders are undoubtedly igneous in origin: but they came to Arabia from a great distance away, pushed out of the sea along with the Hajar Mountains.

Elsewhere in the Arabian Peninsula, there is evidence of volcanic activity millions of years ago. In north-west Arabia, for instance, geologists have found vast areas of solidified lava-flows. In *The Empty Quarter*, St John Philby describes his discovery of the ruined city of Wabar out in the desert. It was said to have been destroyed in fire by heaven because of the pride and licentiousness of its mythical king — a story that would have been only a little more impressive than the volcanic reality.

"I looked down, not upon the ruins of an ancient city, but into the mouth of a volcano, whose twin craters, half filled with drifted sand,

Stones blackened by desert varnish on a rocky slope.

lay side by side surrounded by slag and lava outpoured from the bowels of the earth... They did bear an absurd resemblance to the tumbled remnants of manmade castles," said Philby.

Nearly 60 years later, the British explorer, Ranulph Fiennes, led another expedition which discovered what is believed to be the lost city in southern Oman.

The movement of the Hajar Mountains, though, is worthy of a legend itself. They fascinate geologists because rocks like those in the Hajar, made up of volcanic lavas, oozes, and ocean crust, are usually found below the sea. The Hajar Mountains are an example of the steady, irresistible shifting of the whole peninsula.

The theory goes that they must have been formed some sixty-five million years ago, deep under the sea that's now known as the Indian Ocean. Then, as more lava poured out of the sea bed and forced it apart, the rocks that were to become the Hajar range were shifted over another twenty million years towards the Arabian Peninsula. As they collided with the Arabian landmass, they were thrust on top of it like one gigantic plate sliding over another, in a series of structures referred to by geologists as 'nappes'.

That process, too, will have taken millions of years: and finally, with the rocks from the sea bed now high and dry on the land, they will have been folded and contorted in another series of massive upheavals to create the existing mountains.

The evidence of those upheavals can be seen all over the mountain range. Near Dibba, for example, the green schist rocks, formed millions of years ago by a combination of heat and pressure, clearly show in the rock strata how they were folded up.

Often, the squeezing and pressure changed the black oceanic rocks beyond recognition: the green ophiolites and brown gabbros of the dark mountains south of Dibba and Masafi are both the end product of the same ancient lavas.

Jebel Hafit

Some distance away from the Hajar Mountains, the great mass of Jebel Hafit juts up into the sky above the flat expanse of desert around Al Ain. It's another remnant from millions of years ago, from the times before the Arabian Peninsula began to shift away from Africa, and vast tracts of the region were underwater, in what is now called the Tethys Sea.

The principle is simple: flat slabs of limestone, laid down under the sea, were squeezed over millions of years until, at a weak point, they reared up in a massive fold — a structure known to geologists as an anticline, and often associated with oil-bearing rocks. But the domed summit of the fold has long since eroded and, because the harshness and aridity of the region provides little

Jebel Hafit.

Volcanic rocks of the Hajar Mountains near Hatta.

Immense forces created the Hajar Mountains millions of years ago.

water to smooth and wash away the sharp edges, it has left a jagged series of rocks around its rim. It is practically the skeleton of an anticline.

The drive towards it out of Al Ain is stunning. Huge slabs of limestone are tilted at about 70° to the horizontal, almost like teeth sticking up out of the ground. The lack of soil or vegetation makes the rock formation very clear as the road twists up through the smaller rocks which are scattered around the main rock face.

It's the colours and textures which strike a visitor, though: the deep pinks and reds of the limestone, and the rough, flaky surface of the rock, compared with the smooth concrete that has been used to support the sides of the winding road. Here and there, veins of pink and purple marble meander down a rock face.

The hillside is even more barren than the sandy desert that surrounds it. Only the occasional hardy, stunted bush manages to survive on the porous limestone which allows whatever rain does fall to filter straight into the rock. The steep slopes, too, mean that any rain that does remain on the surface simply drains away down the mountainside.

The drainage from the mountain can be seen clearly from the top. Scrubby vegetation gathers around the channels which branch out from the base of the rock, spreading out into the sandy desert, where the water evaporates in the sun.

When we travelled up Jebel Hafit, work was under way on a new palace to be built right at the summit: it will probably be a good place to enjoy the view from, as it's only in the early morning that the haze usually clears enough to see the full panorama of the desert.

Even in the haze, though, with the flatness of the surrounding country, and the brutal roughness of the rocks themselves, it's easy to imagine the way that the mountain was forced up out of the sea. Jebel Hafit shows probably more graphically than anywhere else the sheer power of the geological forces that shaped Arabia.

The shifting continent

The huge forces that throw up a mountain range, though, are only a by-product of the energy that is still shaping and shifting whole continents. The movement of the Arabian Peninsula goes back millions of years before the arrival of the Hajar Mountains — possibly some two hundred and fifty million years back. Even geologists, whose word for events that happen ten thousand years apart is 'simultaneous', accept that as a long time and it marks the start of the separation of the Arabian Peninsula from Africa.

Arabia is embedded in a huge rock plate, up to 200 kilometres thick, and for the most part well beyond the range of the oil industry's deepest drilling rigs. The plate shifts over periods of millions of years on top of the denser material below the earth's crust. Exactly what are the immense forces which move not just mountains, but the very continents on which they stand, isn't yet fully understood — one theory is that the intense heat still stored in the centre of the earth sets up convectional currents which build up pressure beneath the rocky plates.

But whatever the forces are, they have inched Arabia away from the African continent, opening up the Red Sea behind it. And they still are edging it forward, at a rate which geologists estimate could be as fast as a centimetre each year, towards the north-east.

That may not sound very fast: but in geological terms it's the equivalent of a four-minute-mile and an even-time 100 metres rolled into one.

Where two plates collide, they may thrust rocks out and upwards to set up mountain ranges, as the Hajar Mountains were thrust up from the sea bed — or they may result in sudden and devastating earthquakes. The movement of the plate which carries the Arabian Peninsula has made the whole area from Turkey through central Iran into an earthquake zone, along the line where one plate meets another. The frequent tremors throughout that region are a direct result of the steady shifting of Arabia towards Iran.

But if the volcanic rocks of the Hajar are the ones which most impress visitors, and which have the most astonishing history, it is the limestones and other sedimentary rocks of the peninsula on which the region's whole prosperity is built.

Oil is the region's most valuable mineral deposit — it's also its newest. Around Sohar, on Oman's Indian Ocean coast, prehistoric man was digging out copper thousands of years ago, and his modern counterparts are still doing the same thing today, to the tune of some 14,000 tonnes a year.

And in some parts of the limestone hills, pressure has turned the original rock into marble. All the Omani Marble Company has to do is hew it from the ground, grind and polish it, and it is ready to lay around the walls and courtyards of

Remnants of an anticline: the view from Jebel Hafit.

Mountains of the Musandam.

the opulent buildings all over the peninsula.

In Musandam and northern Oman, most of the mountains are limestone, formed on the sea bed before the sea retreated. They were thrust up in a gigantic rift some two hundred million years ago — long before the volcanic rocks of the Hajar.

Millions of years ago, the whole area south of Dibba would have been under the sea, with the limestone cliffs of the Musandam Peninsula towering up out of the waters. As those cliffs gradually eroded and collapsed into the sea, the limestone mixed with other rocks on the sea bed to form the distinctive concrete-like conglomerate that is found throughout the mountain ranges.

Like Jebel Huwayyah and the other limestone outcrops of the Hajar, the mountains of Musandam carry fossils as a reminder of their submarine formation but they have also been subject to the weathering of heat and rain as the climate of the region has changed over millions of years. Water, seeping into faults in the mountain and dissolving away the rock, has left the lines of joints and faults clearly visible on the surface. Underground, it has created a pattern of crevices, caverns and passages.

Majlis Al Jinn

Out of Musandam and further down the coast, to the south of Muscat, is the huge Majlis Al Jinn cave, in the Selma Plateau of Jebel Bani Jabir. It was formed in precisely the same way, though on a more impressive scale.

The only way into it is by rope, down one of three drops of up to 160 metres, which lead into a chamber some 310 metres long, 225 metres wide, and over 120 metres high.

It was first discovered in 1983, when W Donald Davison lowered himself into the darkness of a gaping 12-metre by 18-metre hole on the surface.

The cave itself has been formed by the action of underground water over many years, dissolving away the limestone. The three entrances will similarly have been eaten away by surface water seeping through cracks in the rock, although the debris underneath them suggests that there must at some time have been an impressive collapse to open the cave up. Along with the rocks and boulders were the bones of birds and animals which presumably had fallen in or got trapped.

Rock strata at Wadi Sumani near Hatta (above) and in the Musandam mountains (below).

Left: The Majlis Al Jinn, Oman.

Rock pools near Hatta.

Inside, the occasional drip of water through the stone has formed delicate clumps of stalagmites growing upwards from the floor, almost like patches of coral. Because the climate changed and the rains stopped thousands of years ago, however, the seepage channels are mostly dry. It is only after the occasional rains that the drips start up again, gradually eating away far inside the rock and extending the stalagmites below.

Explorations like the one that discovered Majlis Al Jinn — the name means 'Meeting Place of the Spirits' — have a severely practical application in a country where rainfall is scarce and highly valued. By studying the way that surface water seeps into the ground, and the complex routes that it takes underground, engineers can often find ways to get at it and bring it back to the surface for use.

A world without corners

All over the region, both in the volcanic rocks of the Hajar, and in the limestone and the other sedimentary rocks, there are less impressive, but equally interesting examples of erosion. In the imposing setting of an underground river at the village of Al Khatwa, on the edge of the mountains near Buraimi, we practically watched the rocks being shaped by the water.

The whole process is startlingly clear there. As you drive along the road from Buraimi, the bare volcanic rocks on the horizon show the marks of thousands of years of folding, almost as if they had been crumpled in a giant hand.

Nearby, flat and horizontal, lie the layers of conglomerate — rock formed of smaller stones, bound together with lime at the sea bottom, and left behind by the retreating ocean. Its undisturbed strata prove that it must have been laid down long after the original mountains were folded up: the pebbles incorporated into them must originally have been broken away from the volcanic mountains, then weathered and smoothed by the sea, before being formed into slabs of rock.

But in fact, the strata weren't completely undisturbed. Along the line of the river bed, water which had dissolved away the lime binding the conglomerate together had apparently opened up a tunnel through the rock, only to have massive slabs of conglomerate come crashing down into it as the tunnel grew bigger and more unstable.

Elsewhere, at the side of the river bed, huge

slabs had broken away and slipped several metres from their original position. The whole area seemed unsettlingly fragile until you tried to shift one of the great rocks that looked so unstable, only to find that it wouldn't even budge a millimetre.

As we worked our way down the dry wadi bed — still keeping a respectful distance from the sides — the rocks had the look of the highly polished concrete of modern buildings. The water in the wadi, whenever it is in flood with the run-off rain from the surrounding mountains, carries grains of sand which buff and polish the rock faces to a high sheen.

For most of the time, though, the wadi is dry: the water has eaten away at the lime, leaving the river bed porous and leaky. At the edge of one big puddle, we could move a single stone, and then watch the water run ceaselessly into the small depression it had left. The hole never filled up: as fast as water flowed in from the puddle, it seeped out again through the wadi bottom. Unless there is a sudden flood of water, the river flows a metre or more underground, to emerge suddenly and unexpectedly from between two huge rocks.

We followed the stream down between two towering cliffs, which often seemed almost to join high above us. On any normal walk in the Gulf sunshine we would have been glad of the shade: but splashing through cold water up to our waists, we would have welcomed some of that baking sun.

In the dim light left by the overhanging cliffs though, we could see how the river had eroded the rocks as it swirled past.

In places, the whirlpool effect had cleared a circular chamber, while the water eddying further downstream had eaten back into the rocks at the side. A curved arm of rock jutted out, left behind by the two forces, but being worn away itself, ever so slowly, as the river continued its work.

Elsewhere, a harder patch of rock had resisted the erosion and formed a waterfall, or two separate rocks had channelled the water between them, building up its speed and force. Where that had happened, there was a corresponding effect downstream, where the water hit more rock and carved out an overhang.

Everywhere, though, had been buffetted smooth. It was a world without corners.

Khatwa — an underground river.

A route through the mountains, near Nizwa.

THE WADIS

The danger may be infrequent, but the piles of boulders and jagged rocks at the foot of the sheer cliff faces show that it's real enough. A journey through the wadis takes you through a landscape that is slowly crumbling to pieces.

Heavy rains, occasional winds, or simply the constant process of erosion eating away at the rock surface, can bring whole sections of the mountainside crashing down without warning.

For the modern town-dwellers of the Northern Emirates, the wadis provide an exciting day's driving, and a myriad of potential picnic spots; for the few villagers who still live along them, they offer a hard and hopeless livelihood, to be hacked out only with constant and back-breaking work.

And throughout history, for the people of Arabia and beyond, they have provided hard-fought routes through otherwise impassable country.

Centuries ago, rivers flowed constantly down the wadi-beds, carrying with them rocks, pebbles, and gravel to the edge of the mountain ranges. There, as the rivers spread out over the flat lands and as the speed of their waters diminished, they deposited the stones to form gravel plains dotted with scrubby vegetation, like the ones around Dhaid and Fujairah.

Shallow wadi beds meander across the plains, while looking down on them from the mountainsides, the distinctive fan-shape of the gravel deposited thousands of years ago — known to the locals as a serir — can still be seen.

The wadis, in fact, are practically a map of the region as it once was, when tumbling rivers dragged down the boulders and debris which now fan out, stranded, across the plains below, as they do near Al-Madan and Shwaib.

The rains, of course, ceased. The land dried up and desiccated, and the rivers slowed down.

43

As they did so, they deposited their sediment and gravel further and further back in the valleys — leaving later occasional floods to carve steep-sided canyons into those softer deposits. Travellers along the modern metalled road over the Hajar Mountains towards Dibba can look down from the bridges near Masafi, and see for themselves how the route runs along on top of the soft layers of sediment, and how later erosion has carved out vertical-sided wadis that run under the road.

Elsewhere, rising sea-levels brought marine deposits of sand and lime, cementing together the stones and leaving firmer layers along the wadi bed to be gradually eroded away in their turn.

Where the water has carved its way down to the impermeable base rocks, pools of water gather, like the ones at Hatta, and on the Mahda road. Many of them, fed by underground springs, have water all the year round, and support tiny fish and other water creatures.

In the rocks near Hatta Pools, incidentally, are tunnels, caves and vertical holes like chimneys carved out of the solid rock face. They are just another example of the endless work of water — in this case, it seeps into weaknesses and cracks in the rock, and then erodes the rock away as it drips down.

Where the erosion weakens the rock so much that chunks of it fall away, caves are left behind, carved almost like shrines, in the mountainside.

The pools offer safe and shady places for swimming in the heat of the summer, although they're not as safe today as they used to be. Too many people have taken advantage of them, and now there's a constant danger of stepping on a piece of broken bottle, or a rusty tin can.

Even the irresistible force of erosion takes a long time to deal with the mess left behind by battalions of picnickers. Plastic bottles probably defeat it altogether.

But apart from the perennial pools, it's only after the occasional rains that the wadis flow at all: and then the water can flood down them without warning, tumbling anything out of its way. People, cars — anything in the wadi, when a flash-flood sweeps down it, is likely to be pounded to pieces on the rocks.

Water pools at Wadi Sharm.

A wadi in flood is an impressive, even frightening sight, with the water seeming to seethe and boil as it races over the old river-bed, rolling the boulders from side to side as it passes them — but that's how it used to be all the time.

Today, in fact, the rains don't have to be particularly heavy to cause the sort of floods that tourists and wadi-bashers are always warned about. Because there is no soil and no vegetation in the mountains to absorb the rain as it falls, the water runs straight off into the drainage system provided by the wadis.

Within hours, the dusty wadi bottom can be awash with seething waters.

That speed and unpredictability, coupled with the irresistible force of the waters, has always been the greatest danger of the wadis for travellers. Now, engineers have tried to tame the water with dams and drainage ditches, but even so, the danger remains. Today, perhaps, the risk is slight, and taken in the search for an exciting day's drive,

Right: Flash flood near the Hatta road.
Below: Water erosion at Hatta Pools.

45

Dangers of the wadi, near Masafi.

Flooding in Wadi Qahfi Subakh.
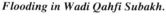

but for centuries, it was an unavoidable and terrifying part of most long journeys in the region.

Almost all of the long-distance trade routes which cross Arabia run along wadis at one point or another, and for centuries the wadi bed provided the only practicable way of crossing the Hajar Mountains. Controlling the route ways gave political power to the different tribes.

Wadi Jizzi

Wadi Jizzi, for instance, runs from Sohar in Oman to Al Ain, and there was no other way of transporting copper from the mines at the end of the wadi to the Gulf coast. Because they controlled the Al Ain oasis, the Abu Dhabi tribes could monitor and control the wadi

Above: Wadi flowers near Masafi.

The twisting track through the gorge towards Wadi Bih: no turn-offs to either side.

Wadi Bih

route. Trade, and the mastery of the different routes, was an important source of their early power and wealth.

Many of today's modern, metalled roads still follow the old wadi routes. And where the roads haven't been made up, drivers thunder along the rough, rocky surfaces in four-wheel drive cars: the main danger now is of meeting another jeep coming round a blind corner at speed. The wadis are used nowadays for having fun rather than as lifelines of trade and commerce but they are also a magnificent display of whole sections of the region's geology, for anyone who looks up from the track at the mountainsides above.

The route from Dibba through Wadi Bih towards Ras Al Khaimah starts in a wide, flat-bottomed wadi where the dust flies up in clouds from the wheels of your car — but then, with a sudden twist, the trail enters a steep-sided gorge. From here on, you can go forward or back: there are no turn-offs to either side.

Jagged rocks glower down from both sides, vegetation is sparse and dried up, and the blistering sun beats down from a cloudless sky.

For most of us, desert landscapes like this are inextricably bound up with childhood memories of cowboys and Indians — and the same forces of heat, barrenness and erosion that formed the dry gulches of the American bad lands have created the wadis of Arabia.

Erosion in the rocks of Jebel Rawdah.

the centuries, and beside them can occasionally be seen the carved-out remnants of an old sedimentary level, looking almost like sections of a derelict roadway, miles from anywhere.

In the gullies which run down the near-vertical cliff faces, boulders and debris fan out towards the valley bottom, and in the solid rock, cracks and fissures run down, splitting the rock-face into gigantic square-sided blocks.

Many of the cracks will have started at weak points in the rock's structure, when the limestone was pushed and tilted upwards to form the mountain range: but, in a parched and scrubby landscape like this, it's hard to remember that almost all of the most noticeable features have been created by water.

Water rushing down from the mountains has carved out the wadi bed itself, and at the same time, it has worn down the boulders, washed and winnowed the fine gravel and sand, and carved away the sediment that had been laid down and compacted before.

Higher on the mountainsides, it has seeped into the cracks and weaknesses in the limestone, gradually wearing them away over the centuries into gullies, pipes and caves, as the water slowly dissolved the rock away along the fault line. It's likely that some of the bigger caves were formed in earlier, wetter areas but there's clear evidence that the process is still going on, even with today's drastically reduced rainfall.

Bulldozers among the rocks

In some places the weakening effect of the water has been too great, and whole slabs of the mountainside have come crashing down into the wadi bed. It obviously didn't happen long ago: they lie there, waiting for the water and the centuries to wear away their jagged corners and smooth them down — and for the moment, they gave the whole massive landscape an unsettlingly fragile quality.

Often, it's possible to spot the place from which a part of the mountain has broken away — a huge pale scar high on the mountainside, gradually healing and darkening with the constant erosion of wind and weather. At other places, you can look up nervously at great overhanging sections of rock that may well be the next to fall.

The track winds up the valley, sometimes on one side of the wadi bed, sometimes on the other, and occasionally running right along it.

On this ride, though, the track heads into the limestone rocks with the wadi bed just below and to the right. Its pale grey rocks and sediment are in marked contrast to the striking horizontal red and orange stripes of the mountainside itself, where the rock strata show clearly along the cliff faces. In the wadi bed are the smooth boulders that have been tumbled down by the water running off the mountains over

It twists and turns, taking sharp corners around great outcrops of rock, and often you can see the marks left behind by the bulldozer, where it has shifted aside the stones and boulders to keep the way clear.

It's an ironic comment on the power of modern machinery: the bulldozer drivers manage to keep a way through the wadi, but when they come to a boulder of any size, all they can do is run the track around it. The mountain always has the last word.

One insignificant-looking cave to the right of the track, well into the wadi, suddenly broadens out when you stand inside it and look upwards, to see a tiny point of light far above you. Hanging over the archway, about the size of a small house, is one block of solid limestone without any apparent support: it seemed a good idea to tip-toe away quietly, and encourage the children not to shout.

From the same place, right on the summit of one peak some 120 metres above us, we could see another huge rectangular block almost ready to fall — a tower of rock, with horizontal cracks running almost all the way through it.

It is a classic example of limestone scenery, but it's hard to take a proper scientific interest when you're trying your hardest not to imagine the effect of dropping a solid chunk of rock the size and weight of several heavy lorries onto the roof of your vehicle.

Major rockfalls are very rare, but it's still pleasant to look back at the narrow sections of the wadi from the relative safety of a wider, more open section.

Sunlight and shadow

It was deep in the gorges, though, that we could best experience the effects of the light: just like the desert, the wadis have their own magnificent effect upon the glaring sun. Here, the high valley sides shade much of the direct sun from the track, and the deep reds and oranges of the rock face reflect it back in muted colours.

Occasionally, looking ahead, we could see the bright sun striking directly onto a mountainside in the distance, giving the landscape its characteristic three-dimensional quality, and setting the different colours off against each other like an impressionist painting.

In the crannies and gullies, black shadows lurk in contrast to the richness of the colours of

Sunlight on the route to Wadi Bih.

the rocks; occasional veins of mineral or marble glisten like jewels; and over it all, like a magnificent vaulted roof, is the deep blue of the sky.

It was impossible not to feel small. And throughout the journey there are constant humbling reminders of how tougher, harder people have come to terms with the harshness of the environment, and turned it to their advantage.

As the merchants and traders made their painstaking way along the wadis centuries ago, they would have passed by tiny villages, which relied for their living on the few flat areas in the wadi bottom and on the slopes above.

The lack of soil in the mountains themselves meant that only those few small patches could be cultivated. A stream ran down from the slopes from time to time, wells could be dug out of the stony ground, and the ingenious falaj system often carried water to the plots from several kilometres away.

Added to that, of course, was a lifetime of hard and backbreaking work — for the reward of a meagre harvest of dates and vegetables, and possibly a tiny herd of goats. Probably their poverty was their only real defence against robbers and bandits although it would have been a daring or foolhardy outsider who chased a villager into the mountains.

Today, if you're lucky, you may get a cheerful wave from the little village, with its brightly painted doors, that hugs the wadi away to the left of the track, carefully above the flood-

Graveyard at the summit of the Wadi Bih route: a reminder of the history of the village.

level. But the villagers, understandably, are unimpressed by the constant stream of wealthy weekend pleasure-seekers that passes through their own hardworking life.

Water tanks, supplied periodically by lorry, make their lives less unpredictable, but even they do little to make them less harsh and unforgiving.

Away from the main settlement, you will see the shelters built for the herdsmen who look after the few hardy goats which pick their way delicately up the mountainside. Often, they've been created from the caves in the rock face, with a few stones piled up around the opening to make a protective wall; at other times, a rusty corrugated iron roof on a rough, stone-built, windowless shack seems a grudging concession to the 20th century.

Later, we came on another settlement. After we had emerged from the gorges through the limestone, through an area where the rocks were more broken up, and the strata were tilted to 25 or 30° to the horizontal, the track seemed suddenly to give up any idea of finding a way through the mountains.

Contours and strata in Wadi Bih: as if the lines have been copied from a map onto the landscape.

Instead, it climbed, in a series of vertiginous hairpin bends which occasionally had the spinning car wheels sending clouds of dust and gravel many metres down into the valley below. The route we'd taken was spread out far behind us. The lines of the rock-strata on the mountains looked exactly as if someone had painstakingly copied the contour lines from the map onto the landscape itself.

Far in the distance, over the hills — great rounded humps these, rather than the jagged landscape that we'd been picking our way through — the Gulf of Oman could just be seen glistening in the late afternoon sun.

Behind us was a tiny clutch of houses built on the summit — deserted now for most of the year, but still a place where families live while they look after their flocks and the few fields they have managed to hack and smooth out of the rocky slopes.

The houses are small, built back into the slope of the mountain, the roofs covered with compacted sand and gravel — as fine a piece of heat-insulation as any modern architect will have come up with in the wealthy towns of Dubai or Abu Dhabi. There are no windows, and if the single television aerial above the silent village is a mark of today, the tiny graveyard among the houses is a reminder of the history of the place.

Above it, the summit of the mountain seems to be almost shivering into tiny blocks as the erosion continues its work on the rock face. Among the houses, the goats wander at will in the quiet.

The switchback road down the other side of the mountains is less impressive, but once again, it was easy to see how the rock had been shaped and weathered.

Rainwater has run off the mountain slopes, smoothing and shaping them, and then forming gullies which cut vertically down, dividing the mountains up into huge rounded blocks. Deep in the gullies, and fanning out below them across the mountain sides, are deposits of weathered rocks and boulders.

The work of erosion is still going on, and as we bumped and shuddered over the rocky floor of the wadi on the other side of the mountains, its irresistible effects were obvious. Stones had been brought down from the mountains above over the previous centuries but that is no more than the slow, steady change you expect to see.

At the end of the wadi, a special dam has been built to stop the rain water running straight off the mountains and cascading away. The idea is that the wall holds the flood back long enough for the rains to seep down into the ground and recharge the water table, so that modern technology can turn what used to be a terrifying flood into a life-giving supply of water.

It all works well — at the moment. But when we drove past, even though there was still water left in the dam from the recent rains, there was also a covering of sand visible on the bottom. It had been winnowed out of the rocks and the slopes by the rain, and washed down the wadi, to be trapped up against the dam wall.

In time, the dam will silt up and need to be dredged clear again... and again... and again.

Like the men with the bulldozers on the other side of the mountain, the engineers who try to control the effects of the rains have an unending job. Erosion doesn't even pause.

Above: A wadi home — Wadi Qahfi Subakh.
Below: After heavy rain a lake forms behind the dam wall at the end of Wadi Bih.

Wadi Dyker, near Muscat.

ALONG THE COASTLINE

Newcomers to Arabia are often surprised by the fruitfulness and variety of the desert, and similarly, few of them appreciate the close links that have bound the Arabs for centuries to the sea. The mistaken view of the region held by many outsiders is that of a barren land made rich only by oil.

Between the desert and the sea though, lies a strip of land that might fulfil their expectations — an area over much of which practically nothing will grow.

Vegetation here consists entirely of halophytes, or salt-resistant plants, such as the mangroves, which secrete surplus salt through pores in their leaves. Naturalists point to the salt-flats as a fascinating treasure-house of plant and animal species — but then, they say much the same about motorway verges and military shooting ranges.

The salt flats, or sabkhas, are the windswept, sterile result of the meeting of the desert and the sea. The occasional rains, which bring flowers and greenery to the desert, generally lie uselessly on top of the sands here, eventually evaporate, and are forgotten. Little grows, little survives, and even movement across the deceptively firm crust on top of the muddy ooze can be dangerous. If Arabia has badlands, they are in the sabkhas.

Even Wilfred Thesiger, who found good things to say about most of his travels across The Empty Quarter, sounded bleak and unenthusiastic when he came to the Sabkha Mutti, between Abu Dhabi and Qatar.

"Camels are always bad on greasy surfaces, so we fastened knotted cords under their feet to stop them from slipping. Here the salt-flats

Al Shaam, near Ras Al Khaimah.

55

Arabian badlands: the sabkha near Dubai.

were divided into three arms by crescent-patterned drifts of sterile white sand. The flats themselves were covered with a crust of dirty salt which threw up a glare into our faces, and, even through half-closed eyes, stabbed deep into my skull. The camels broke through this crust and floundered forward through liquid black mud. It took us five unpleasant, anxious hours to get across..."

And for some people, the Sabkha Mutti has been more than an inconvenience. According to St John Philby, this sabkha was named after a man who was swallowed up, camel and all, in the clinging mud, and that macabre story seems to hang over the whole miserable area. Philby's own impressions, too, were negative to say the least.

"It is three days' journey from end to end on the road to our country. There is neither bush for fuel, nor even stones..." he was warned by his bedu companion. The huge tract of the Sabkha Mutti, some 60 kilometres by 100 kilometres of treacherous and unpredictable slime, was known as a hazard for travellers along the coast route west of Abu Dhabi. People were skilled in using the most unpromising land to the full, but this was truly useless country.

The rising coast

And yet, to anyone interested in how the landscape is formed, the barren, glistening sabkhas have a fascination of their own. Finding them 150 metres above sea level, as you can at Hofuf, is a reminder of how the coast of the Arabian Peninsula has slowly risen over the last few thousand years. And, just as you can with the sand dunes in the desert, you can watch the sabkhas forming, and the shape of the coastline changing.

It's not comfortable. Near Dohat Dhalum, south of Dhahran, you sit cupping your hands round your eyes as the stinging grains of sand swirl in the wind. The sand whips into the sea, gradually filling in the bay, and creating a flat, low-lying plain, smoothed by the sea, and killed by the salt. It is dead land.

As the water has evaporated away, it has left salt behind, which causes the sterility of the landscape. When the weather is dry — which is most of the year — moisture is sucked up out of the sand, leaving its deposit of salt crystals on the surface, and forming a hard, crusty layer which glistens in the sun.

At other times, when the rains come, the sabkhas may be covered in still, leaden pools, because the water table, saturated with seawater, is so close beneath the surface.

Along the coast, many of the salt flats show clear lines where the sealine used to be. Because the action of the sea has left them so flat — they slope at a rate of something less than half-a-metre in every kilometre — they're permanently vulnerable to being swamped again by the sea in stormy weather.

Even more treacherous, though, are the sabkhas made up of thin, almost liquid, mud rather than sand. The mud is formed by algae and other organisms in the shallows along the edge of the shore, and then, left in the sun and packed down by traffic, it dries out to the consistency of asphalt.

More often, though, it's gradually covered by sand blown onto it by the wind. At a depth of one metre, the experts say, the sand will form a solid enough layer to support a moving vehicle — though it's not, I must admit, an experiment I cared to try, even in the cause of science.

Rain doesn't change its appearance — but once it's wet, it softens like quicksand, leaving any vehicle foolish enough to have taken a chance on it helplessly stranded wheel-deep in treacly mud.

The west coast of the Musandam.

The sabkhas are an unprepossessing mixture of land and sea: but along most of the Gulf coastline, the edge of the Arabian Peninsula is ill-defined and uncertain, scattered with islands, reefs, and shoals, as if the land can't make up its mind where to end.

It's a result of the way the sea was made. On the other side of the Gulf, where the collision between the rocky plates actually took place, the Zagros Mountains were formed in Iran, and the Gulf was carved out much more deeply. But on this side, the land just slopes gently down to the water's edge, until the mountains of Musandam, north of Ras Al Khaimah, form their own rampart sticking out into the Gulf.

There, in Oman and the far north of the Emirates, is a very different coast. The road into Oman out of Ras Al Khaimah has been blasted out of the sheer mountain face, then built up out of reach of the sea on a bed of boulders, rubble and gravel. For half a kilometre or so, in between the two tiny border posts, it clings perilously to the side of the mountain, with the water lapping at its manmade rampart.

Above it, the crumpled limestone shows clearly the marks of the stresses and folding that formed Musandam. In some places, the rock is being painstakingly quarried away, to be shipped off from a small purpose-built port; elsewhere, whole strata have sheered away, leaving the rocks beneath smooth and bare to the wind.

Nearby, almost in the shadow of the cliffs we watched a group of a dozen or so fishermen hauling in their nets in the bay. After about an hour's muscle-wrenching work, heaving against the weight of the water and the tide, they had pulled out a net full of fish that would have filled a small van. The fish — mostly no more than four or five centimetres long, destined to be salted and sold by the kilo — gasped and threshed inside the nylon threads of the net, slumped on the shore. The same skills and the same techniques had been used for centuries: it was a reminder of how closely intertwined the history of the peoples of the Gulf has been with the sea.

The search for fresh water

What they have always needed, of course, is fresh water. On one of the islands further up the Gulf, the settlement of Abu Dhabi grew up when sweet water was discovered there some 200 years ago. The process was repeated in reverse at Umm Al Quwain, where the settlement moved off the island of Siniyyah and onto its present site when the well on Siniyyah ran dry.

It's a reminder of how, in the desert or on the coast, in tents or in settlements, the Arabs have for centuries followed fresh water. It's only in the last few decades, with the development of efficient desalination plants, that the tie has been eased.

But all the Northern Emirates have grown up looking to the sea, built round creeks and inlets. In between Abu Dhabi and Umm Al Quwain, after an expanse of flat, monotonous coastal plain, comes Dubai, built around the most perfect natural harbour in the Gulf, and still relying for its prosperity on the trade which grew up around the Creek.

Like many of the individual features of the landscape, the creeks show the countries of the Gulf as they once were: in this case, warm, wet lands, with rivers running from the inland mountains out to the sea.

Thousands of years ago, the rivers which flowed around Dubai ran into a large freshwater lake which stretched some 45 kilometres inland from the present lagoon. Today, all that's left of that are the chalk, limestone and dolomite rock, much of it quarried out in the last

Harvesting the Gulf.

Flamingoes in Dubai Lagoon.

few decades to supply the builders who have created modern Dubai.

The creeks of the Gulf coastline are the drowned remnants of river estuaries — flooded by the rising sea, and deserted by the waters that once tumbled into them.

Or, almost deserted. From the air, traces of wadi beds, marked by the growth of acacia trees, can still be seen stretching across the desert towards the creeks. And the rivers do still flow occasionally, as if remembering what the country used to be like. At Badar Al Ali, north of Umm Al Quwain, the road crosses a wadi on a bridge which has been swept away several times in flood waters, and at Ras Al Khaimah too, the river sometimes comes suddenly to life again, draining the rains off the mountains.

Further south, where the mountains are further inland, and the rivers would have further to go, the land is dry. All that remains of its ancient natural drainage system is the pattern of coastal creeks. But it's not just the failure of the rains over the centuries that has dried up the rivers: as the massive plate on which the whole Arabian Peninsula is formed tilts gradually to the east — a process we described in

another chapter — the Gulf coast is rising all the time. There are fewer and fewer paths for the water down to the sea.

The Lagoons

Instead of rivers, we now have lagoons, where seawater has collected at the top end of the creeks. The flatness of the land means that the water covers a wide area; and there simply isn't enough force in the tides to scour out an efficient natural drainage channel. In many places, men have helped what nature has failed to achieve: the Sharjah lagoon was deepened to create a lake, and improve the flow in and out of the creek, and similar work was started on Dubai's lagoon as well. There, sand from the newly dredged lagoon was used to build up new land on freshly drained sabkhas — until the workers reached the far end of the lagoon, when the work became prohibitively expensive. It's unlikely that anyone realised it at the time, but the benefit of that was that it left an ideal environment for the flamingoes and other wildlife that now inhabits the lagoon.

But if the Emirates are built around the creeks, it's only with constant work that they are kept fully open to the sea. One thing that is clear from the landscape in the Gulf is that nothing is fixed — and the creeks are changing faster than most other features.

The ebb and flow of the tides alone, scouring the creeks out twice a day, would probably stop them from disappearing, but the combined effects of winds and tides together would leave them shallow, shifting waterways, with ever-changing navigation channels that the most experienced pilot would be unable to cope with.

Waves are forced by the prevailing winds along the coast in a northerly direction, carrying the sand and rounded grains of lime from the beaches with them, to form sand bars, spits, and islands across the mouths of the creeks and all along the shoreline. In addition to that, ebbing tides sucking the water out of the creeks tend to deposit still more sand over the sandbars left by the waves. Sand under the water, just like sand under the wind, has its own momentum:

once a sand bar is formed, it will naturally grow just like a dune.

But, just to make things even more treacherous for the long suffering Arab sailors, every now and then a storm will sweep away a sand bar, or shift its position. It then lies like a trap beneath the sea level, waiting for an incautious pilot who believes that the navigation channels he thought he knew so well may not have changed.

The problem is at least understood today, and, even though it won't go away, it no longer represents a threat to shipping. Modern engineers, in fact, have found ways to take advantage of the action of wind and waves, and reclaim valuable land from the sea.

We look elsewhere, of course, at the mountains: down around the coastline are a few of their poor relations.

Racing dhows in the Gulf.

Jebel Ali

The Arabic word 'jebel' may mean 'mountain', but in the case of Jebel Ali, it might more accurately be translated as 'molehill'. It's never going to impress a visitor by sheer size, even though its gently sloping sides, topped by communications equipment, broadcasting aerials and satellite dish, do dominate the flat landscape for miles around.

From the summit — if molehills have summits — anyone ready for a gentle walk up will enjoy a panoramic view of Jebel Ali port, the biggest man-made harbour in the world. For the idle, it's ideal, because the surrounding area is so flat that it has all the advantages of a mountain, without the drawback of a long climb up.

But Jebel Ali has an intrinsic interest far beyond its size. Crystals of gypsum, some of them glittering like diamonds three centimetres across, make the rocks glisten white, yellow and red in the sun; deposits of sulphur give the whole area an almost unreal yellowish tinge.

These are rocks that belong far below the surface, formed from lavas, sandstone, and ancient limestones. The blown sand that covers most of the ground makes it look like little more than a swelling in the desert, but the debris that is scattered around has come to the surface from thousands of metres below.

Jebel Ali, in fact, is the remnant of a salt plug, a sort of poor man's volcano, that has forced the ancient, low-lying rocks up to the surface through a weak point in the sedimentary layers above them. They're not an uncommon feature in this part of the world, because the whole area is so geologically unstable that there are plenty of faults through which the salt can find its way to the surface.

Jebel Dhanna, near Abu Dhabi, is another salt plug, where oil companies have taken advantage of the firmer, rocky ground to mount their storage tanks. The elevation of the site means that oil can be piped by gravity down to the shore and out to the waiting tankers.

Islands in the Gulf

Often, as at Abu Mousa off Sharjah, Sir Bani Yas and Das Island, the rocks have been forced up out of the sea bed, creating islands in the

Jebel Ali — an important centre for telephone, radio and television equipment.

Approaching Musandam coast.

Gulf. Other islands have been formed by the growth of coral on top of smaller, underwater heaps of rocks from salt plugs.

The ages, the distances, and the pressures involved in the creation of these piles of rubble are almost inconceivable. Layers of ancient salt, up to 700 million years old, lie at depths of 5,000 metres and more below the surface. The immense pressure of the rocks above forces the salt to find weak spots, and drives it up towards the surface like an oil well — dragging with it fragments of the rocks from below.

Often, because the same points of weakness that allowed the salt out of the ground can allow oil to the surface too, the salt plugs are related to the development of oil fields. Because of the way they bring otherwise inaccessible rocks and minerals up towards the surface, the salt plugs played a part in mining and industry centuries before people began looking for oil.

Sulphur extracted from the gypsum was once used in making gunpowder. In the past too, the columns of salt left behind in the ground were often dug out and used, as is reported to have been done on the island of Sir Abu Nuair.

In the Iranian mountains, there are 'glaciers' of salt running down out of groups of salt plugs on the surface, but on this side of the Gulf, the surface salt, mingled in with the rocks dragged up from below, is quickly washed away — leaving behind it, essentially, a pile of rubble.

Thousands of years of weathering and erosion may smoothe and shape the pile; desert sand will blow onto it and all but cover it, as it has at Jebel Ali.

But the rocks will always remain out of place — fragments from miles below the surface, kicking about on the top and glittering in the unaccustomed sun.

OFF THE COAST

The evening light had sapped the colour out of the rocky mountains that line the eastern coast of the UAE, and they were banked up almost like storm clouds along the horizon. In front of them, as our boat made its way slowly back to Fujairah Port, the waters of the Gulf of Oman were calm and dark.

The fishing hadn't been a particularly successful venture — even in the rich fishing grounds around the Arabian Peninsula, you need a certain amount of skill to tempt your prey onto your line — but the trip had been worthwhile simply for the different view it gave of the country.

Along much of the Gulf, the shoreline of the Emirates lies low along the horizon, barely visible above the sea. An occasional skyscraper or storage tank may attract the eye, but it is for the most part a featureless, drab line running alongside the deep blue of the water. It's only when the sun strikes directly onto the land that the oranges and reds of the sand flash back across the sea, with some clue to the rich colours of the inland landscape.

From the Arabian Sea, of course, it is different. Dark mountains sweep almost down to the water's edge, barely leaving room for the coast road to squeeze its way through between mountains and sea. From miles offshore, the rocks still rear up above the water, their colours gradually fading back towards the horizon.

It's a sight that must have become familiar and welcome to the Arab sailors from Oman and the trading ports of the Gulf as they returned home after voyages that would often have taken them away for months, and sometimes for years.

Although the Europeans' image of the Arab

Harbour sunset, Khor Fakkan.

65

Fishermen near Dibba.

world is inextricably bound up with the sands of the desert, and the camels that once carried the bedu tribes across them, the sea has always been an important part of life on the Arabian Peninsula.

Long before Europeans rounded the Cape of Good Hope to 'discover' what lay beyond it, Arab traders were sailing thousands of miles to Sri Lanka, the East Indies and beyond. Dead reckoning, accurate instruments to read the stars and the sun, and a long tradition of seamanship had taken them all the way to the rich markets of China centuries earlier: the stories of the seven voyages of Sindbad the Sailor are the gathered-up legends of a seafaring people.

Occasionally, undoubtedly, those seafarers took advantage of the wealthy merchantmen making their own way back to Europe from India — although the British stories of the notorious pirates of the Gulf are now being questioned. The fact is that on the high seas two or three

of the Gulf for their livelihood, had barely ventured out of sight of land — though anyone who banked on catches such as ours to make a living would have lived a meagre life indeed.

Food from the sea

For centuries, the people of the Arabian Coast have taken their food from the sea. Near Ras Al Khaimah are the remains of communities who once lived on the mangrove swamps around Jazirat Al Hamra.

All that is left of them today, pathetically, is their rubbish heaps — piles of old shells and the remains of marine animals from 5,000 or more years ago — but the little fishing fleets still put out each day from villages scattered up and down the coast.

Today, too, the farmers of the coast still look to the sea. Around Ras Al Khaimah, they grow some 40 or 50 varieties of dates, and use dried

Dhows returning to Dubai Creek from the open sea, as they have for generations.

centuries ago, whether a ship was a trader or a pirate sometimes depended largely on which end of its guns you were standing at.

The bounty of the sea often came in the form of fish, sometimes in the form of rich cloths and treasures from the Far East — and occasionally, no doubt, in the form of booty originally bound for some quite different port. Sailors were not known for their particularity.

We, like many of the fishermen who have relied on the Arabian Sea and the sheltered waters sardines from the fishermen's catch as a cheap and effective fertiliser for the palm trees.

And the sea has given the Arabs more than food. For many years, until the development of cultured pearls in the 1930s, this was the centre of the world's pearling industry. Fleets of sambouks (dhows) sailed from Bahrain and other ports at the start of the diving season in June to harvest the oysters from the shallow waters of the Gulf.

For the divers who went down 20 metres or more, often 120 times a day, the depth must have been crippling. They had no complex charts, like modern divers, to work out the levels of harmful nitrogen building up in their blood, and only one day in ten in which to rest from the constant work.

Pearling was a hard life, but it was possible only because the Gulf, in comparison to other seas, is extremely shallow indeed — it averages only 35 metres, and it's seldom more than 80 metres deep, except for a few areas around Qatar and near the Strait of Hormuz. The deepest point comes near the southern tip of Qeshm Island, off Bandar Kingeh on the Iranian coast, where the natural formation of the sea bed and the scouring action of the

currents as they round the elbow of the Gulf combine to give a depth of some 110 metres.

For the most part, though, its shallowness is something that not just the pearlers, but also the oilmen, had reason to be thankful for: much of the oil of the Arabian Peninsula is situated conveniently below the land, but even the reserves out in the Gulf are relatively easy to reach.

The deepwater operations of the North Sea, which make British oil so expensive to take out of the ground, are totally unnecessary in an environment where divers with modern equipment can work comfortably on the sea bed. Oil wells in warm, shallow waters are more easily drilled, more easily established, and more easily maintained.

And in the future, too, the sea will bring prosperity to the region. Plans at the moment to develop tourism in the Emirates and Oman rest to a considerable extent on the hospitable coastline, with its long, sandy beaches.

On the Gulf Coast, limestone and seashells have been ground down to form the white, shimmering sands which are so beloved by the

Coastal flats near Jazirat Al Hamra.

Sandy beach at Umm Suqeim, Dubai.

photographers who compile the tourist brochures — and on the other side, by the Arabian Sea, the dark volcanic sand gives a distinctive, chocolate brown colour to the beaches.

And the tourists will also be attracted by the fishing, I thought bitterly, as we tied up our boat in Fujairah port and lifted out our empty bag.

Like everything else in the region, the Gulf itself has been formed and shaped by the steady shifting of the continents.

The movement of the Arabian Peninsula away from Africa has opened up the Red Sea behind it — and in front, where two massive plates of rock collide, it has built up the Zagros Mountains of south-west Iran.

The basin which was formed over millions of years, as the mountains were reared up in the collision, became the Arabian Gulf.

That, in geological terms, was just about the day before yesterday — or, to be more precise, some five million years ago. In the same terms, the present form of the Gulf was settled about a minute and a half ago — perhaps some 60,000 years.

Between those two times, the water fluctuated wildly, with the movement of the land and with the effects of the Ice Ages. The ice, of course, never reached this region but 20,000 years ago, when sub-zero temperatures had extended the polar ice caps, the level of the seas all round the world dwindled rapidly. At that time, the Gulf was no more than a wide, shallow river-valley, carrying the estuary of the combined flows of the Tigris and Euphrates Rivers.

Below today's sea-level are submarine platforms and the drowned valleys of rivers that once ran down to a much smaller sea. But shells and marine fossils have been found far above today's sea level as well. After the Ice Ages, as the ice-caps melted, the sea levels rose again — bringing water into the Gulf as high as 150 metres above its present level.

Between those two extremes, as the climate of the region changed and the land shifted, the waters have risen and fallen. Exactly which changes were the result of greater rainfall, and which the result of the growth of mountains, and changes on the sea-bed, is still a matter of debate among geologists. It's clear, though, that the changes were far reaching and, in geological terms at least, speedy.

Legends and memories

One scientist even suggests that a dim folk memory of these rapid changes in sea level, passed on from father to son around the Arab world, could be responsible for the account of Noah's Flood in Genesis.

"The waters prevailed exceedingly upon the earth: and all the high hills that were under the whole heaven were covered. Fifteen cubits upward did the waters prevail; and the mountains were covered," says the Old Testament.

Those 15 cubits, in less poetic but more scientific terms, suggest a rise in the level of the waters of something between seven and eight metres — a deluge indeed!

There's no doubt that all those things and more have happened along the shores of the Gulf during its history, or that they are still going on. But the changes take thousands of years at the very least to become apparent: geological measurements over the past few decades have established that the Gulf Coast of the UAE is slowly rising, while the Gulf Coast of Musandam is gradually sinking.

At a rate of half-a-centimetre a year, it's not likely to turn into a sort of geological somersault — but it has changed the level of the mountains by something like 60 metres in the last ten thousand years. At the same time, because the western coastline of the Gulf has such a gentle slope, a relatively small rise or fall in the water level over a period can affect a large area on the ground.

And the changes in water level have had marked effects on the whole geological make-up of the region, quite apart from the purely cosmetic effects of terracing and the sea erosion of mountain slopes which are now far inland.

Underground springs, working their way through the limestone base when the land was dry, emerge now far out to sea. One legend, which you can believe or not, tells of a camel which fell into a spring, only to reappear in the

Limestone rocks of the Musandam.

An underwater world.

A fishing dhow anchored in a quiet cove near the Strait of Hormuz.

ocean — presumably dead, although a miraculously preserved camel would make the whole tale only a little less unbelievable.

Harder to ignore, though, are the accounts of Ibn Batuta, one of the most famous Arab seamen of the 14th century. He reports that sailors would dive into the salt waters of the Gulf carrying leather bags, in which they would bring up fresh water from springs on the sea bed.

Portuguese sailors, centuries later, claim to have supplied themselves with fresh water from the same source using pumps.

Salty waters of the Gulf

For the most part, though, the Gulf is one of the saltiest seas in the world — a direct result of the hot, dry climate. Because there is very little rainfall in the surrounding arid lands, it loses much more water through evaporation than it gains from freshwater sources such as rivers and streams. Since the evaporated water leaves its salt behind, the seawater has gradually become saltier and saltier.

The narrowness of the Strait of Hormuz prevents any significant exchange of water between the Gulf and the Arabian Sea. In fact, recent measurements show that there is a constant current of salty water passing out of the Gulf at the bottom of the Strait, while lighter, fresher water from outside moves in on the surface — but the movement isn't enough to affect the great disparity between the two seas.

It's a pattern, in fact, which is repeated in the Strait of Gibraltar, where the Mediterranean meets the North Atlantic. It is only the higher rainfall, feeding rivers to supply the Mediterranean, that stops it becoming as salty as the Gulf.

This saltiness has a great effect on the marine life of the entire region. The growth of coral, for instance, is severely restricted in the Gulf by comparison with the waters of the Arabian Sea only a few miles away. Only a few species can survive — even though those that can are plentiful enough, and sharp enough, to pose something of a threat to unwary swimmers.

In fact, the formation of the Gulf is repeated in miniature in the famous Inland Sea of Qatar, a large lagoon at the base of the peninsula. Like the Gulf itself, it is a drowned estuary — in this case, the estuary of an ancient river which flowed from the Asir Mountains of Saudi Arabia across the continent to join up with the combined waters of the Tigris and the Euphrates. The river itself, of course, is long gone — it flowed twenty thousand years ago, during the Ice Age, when the Gulf was lower, and the climate was wetter.

But on the hills immediately to the south of the sea there remains a fascinating memory of Arabia as it was thousands of years ago — river gravel, formed of granite, quartz and chips of slate, 60 metres above sea level, where no river gravel ought to be.

It was carried down from the distant Asir Mountains by the river that ran all those years ago down to the sea — and is left there now, hundreds of kilometres from its source, stranded by the movement of the land and the changes of the climate.

The Inland Sea, more correctly known as the Khawl Al Udayd, is all that remains of the river. It's an irregularly shaped lagoon, about 25 kilometres across and about the same distance long, with a narrow barrier of rock and coral about a metre below the surface cutting it off from the rest of the Gulf.

The movement of the tides is enough to prevent the entrance from silting up and separating the lagoon completely from the sea — but, like many of the features of the landscape in this part of the world, the Khawl Al Udayd is gradually changing, and will eventually disappear. To the north, a belt of sand dunes is gradually moving south in front of the prevailing winds.

As the barchans slowly march towards it, you can watch the sands of the desert blowing irresistibly into the lagoon. It has a long way to go — in places, the water is around 25 metres deep — but eventually, the Khawl Al Udayd will be filled up.

The desert will have reclaimed the land, and the ancient river that drained the mountains on the other side of Arabia will be no more than a memory in a textbook. Only the gravels will remain, hundreds of kilometres away from the nearest similar rocks, and a full 60 metres above the sea, where they ought not to be.

Inland Sea, Qatar.

WEATHER IN THE GULF

"You can have no idea," he said, with a weary but good-natured smile, "how boring it can get being told that you must have the easiest job in the world."

Steve, the weatherman at Dubai Television, prepares the regular nightly forecasts from an array of meteorological reports from all round the region. "And remember," he remarks, with the air of a man telling a joke he has told a thousand times before, "there are only so many different ways you can say 'Warm and sunny'."

He was, of course, being characteristically modest. The weather in the Gulf region may generally be reliable enough for expat social butterflies to plan their barbecues months in advance, but people want, and get, a lot more detail from their weather forecasts than a simple reassurance that the sun's going to shine again tomorrow.

And the weather does more than encourage an *alfresco* social life and increase the sale of charcoal and firelighters. It helps to create and modify the landscape: strong winds move the sands of the desert, shifting dunes and smothering wadis and inlets; airborne grains of sand blast and scour the mountain rocks; sudden downpours of rain sculpt the contours of the wadis; and the ever-present blazing sun bakes the sabkhas to a salty crust.

But here, as everywhere else, the landscape and the coastline play their part in creating the weather as well.

The Gulf itself, losing its daytime heat more slowly than the land around it, sucks air off the desert, and produces light breezes which blow off the land during the night. South-east or easterly winds, blowing across the deserts of the Rub' Al Khali, may bring a dry heat, without

Storm over Hamriya Beach.

75

humidity, even to the coast. They may too, incidentally, by lifting the fine sand high into the air, paint the stunning red and orange streaks of a Gulf sunset over the sea.

But the Gulf's weather is often produced hundreds of kilometres away. During the winter, for example, the complex meteorological charts may show a reassuring band of low pressure over the sea along the coast of Iran for days on end, bringing light north-westerly winds with it.

Far away, though, in the temperate regions of the Northern Hemisphere, the cold air from the North Pole is buffeting into the warmer air spreading out from the equator. The disturbance caused as hot air and cold collide in the atmos-phere produces a turmoil of low pressure and high pressure areas and a series of fronts and low-pressure troughs which, constantly forming and shifting, bring Europe its characteristically changeable weather.

These weather systems are drawn inexorably southwards towards the warm, lower pressure areas around the equator, and are forced eastwards by the rotation of the earth — and as they eventually make their way south-east through the Gulf region, they bring sudden changes in the winds and the weather here with them.

Early morning over the dunes near Al Awir: long wispy cirrus clouds begin to form.

Plans for a desert drive in Dubai may be ruined by a clash between hot and cold air somewhere over Poland.

As the front approaches, it may be preceded by a brisk south-easterly wind, the sharqi — a name taken simply from the Arabic word for 'east' — which is likely to whip up rising sand for a while. The cloud will thicken, usually leading up to thunderstorms and even gusts of gale-force wind just ahead of the front.

After the front, though, comes the shamal wind. That's from the Arabic word for 'north', but in fact, its direction varies around the region, depending on the shape of the Gulf, which channels and directs the wind.

Around the head of the Gulf, from Kuwait as far south as Bahrain, it does come from the north, but as it follows the sweep of the shore-line, it blows generally from a west-north-westerly direction around Dubai and Sharjah, and from the south-west away towards Pakistan as it passes through the Strait of Hormuz.

It lasts for anything up to five days before the arrival of the next front, often bringing with it sand and dust from the northern Gulf, although it's not necessarily a strong wind.

More feared by fishermen here is the sudden and unpredictable nashi wind, which blows up over southern Iran as cold air spills down from the high pressure area over the mountains, forcing its way out into the Gulf. Usually, this process brings no more than a few light offshore breezes near the coast, but a sudden increase in pressure caused, for example, by a cold front moving quickly down from the north, will send gusts of 50 knots or more screaming out over the sea.

The wind can blow up in a matter of minutes, often carrying thick clouds of dust south or south-west out to sea, and maybe accompanied by hail or thunderstorms.

It's most frequent near the Iranian coast, although it can blow as far south as Dubai, or even Abu Dhabi. Usually, the wind doesn't last for long, but by the time it reaches the southern coastal waters, it may have whipped up steep seas of an intensity that is mercifully rare in the well-protected waters of the Gulf.

Apart from the remnants of occasional cyclones which may blow up out beyond the Strait of Hormuz in the northern Arabian Sea around April or November, the nashi is probably the

Storm over Dubai.

closest the Gulf region comes to a dangerous and unpredictable storm.

Mountain storms

During the summer months, the day's likely to start with a temperature in the mid-eighties and it will rise inexorably to 100°F or more during the day. The sun will shine for 10 hours a day, and newcomers who try to cool off in the sea will be disappointed: the coastal water in mid-summer usually heats up to around 90°F.

But the summer, too, can bring its surprises. From April to November, there will be weeks on end with barely a cloud in the sky, broken without warning up in the mountains by torrential rain, deafening claps of thunder, and sudden savage gusts of wind. Dry wadis may turn in a matter of minutes into raging torrents as the water, running straight off the rocky, impervious mountain slopes, rushes downwards back towards the sea.

A few kilometres away though, people may still be sweltering under a pitiless sun. Perhaps Ras Al Khaimah may feel an occasional mountain shower, but summer storms like this stay close to the hills.

Again, it is conditions far away that cause the sudden break in the weather. Over Oman or Iran, air pressure may rise slightly for a spell, sending light, moist winds scudding westward

Sunrise near Dibba.

out across the Gulf of Oman towards the mountains. There, they are forced to rise, pelting the land with heavy rain as they cool rapidly in the upper air.

But the ground has been baked by weeks of uninterrupted sunshine, and heat radiates up to warm the lower atmosphere. As the temperature builds up towards mid-day, it helps to form towering cumulo-nimbus clouds, sending strong and unpredictable down-draughts blowing across the land.

That, though, is the exception. Day by day, the light winds generally blow off the sea for most of the day, swinging round at night to blow in the other direction. The air heats up more quickly over the land than it does over the sea,

because the water absorbs the heat of the sun more effectively. As the air gets hotter, the pressure drops, sucking in winds from over the Gulf.

At night, though, the reverse is true. Land changes temperature more quickly than the water: the air above it, therefore, cools down more quickly than the air over the sea, and as it does, the density and pressure of the air increase. At dusk, the wind drops almost as if it were intentionally providing a few minutes of stillness for people to appreciate the sunset.

Then the temperature change begins to take effect, the warm breezes blow gently out to sea, and it's time to go home.

Landscape and weather

It sounds as if summer in the Gulf should be heaven: but everyone knows that it isn't. It's not the heat that can make it uncomfortable so much as the humidity, which often reaches 100 per cent.

Once again it's the landscape, the shape of the Gulf, and the direction of the winds that produce the weather.

The westerly or north-westerly winds bring hot, clinging weather onto the coastline of the Emirates, as they carry in the moisture they have collected over the sea. Winds from the east, of course, blow off the desert: they may be hotter, but they also are generally more comfortable, as they give below-average humidity. It's only later in the day that conditions may get stickier as the afternoon sea-breezes bring in the moisture they have gathered just off-shore earlier in the day.

Overnight, as the damp winds hit the cooler air over the land, the moisture in them will condense suddenly. If there is no wind to clear it away, early morning motorists will find their journey bedevilled by sudden dangerous patches of mist and fog — at least until the heat of the sun makes the moisture evaporate.

In either case, by the time the winds get further inland, towards the mountains, the moisture has been lost, which helps to explain the popularity of Hatta and the mountains for siting summer retreats in the days before air-conditioning.

Whether or not they understood why conditions changed so suddenly, the people who lived here years ago appreciated the relationship between the landscape and the weather. The occasional downpour from a summer storm was a small price to pay for day to day comfort.

CHANGING THE LANDSCAPE

One of the attractions of the Gulf region for anyone who wants to study the landscape and the way it is made is that man has made such an insignificant impression upon it.

The nomadic lifestyle of the bedu left the desert landscape unchanged for generations, and over most of the region, even today, the desert has swallowed up every trace of humanity leaving nothing behind.

Where there used to be small settlements, there are now several big towns which have grown rapidly over the last 20 years. Occasionally, like Dubai and Sharjah, they have joined together to form a continuous ribbon development along the coastline, which may prove to be a pattern for the future, as the economy of the region continues to grow.

Where once only a few camels plodded painstakingly across the sand, metalled roads slice through the landscape of the Emirates and the rest of the region. Apart from the impact they make themselves, they carry people quickly and easily to places which, only a few years ago, were virtually inaccessible.

But the deserts of the Gulf are vast: despite the huge growth of the past two decades, the towns and the roads still cover only an infinitesimal part of the countryside. Even inside them, unusually for modern cities, there are still untouched areas of sand and occasional palm trees, reminders of what was here before.

Everywhere, of course, man leaves more than footprints behind him, and the Emirates are no different from the rest of the world. Particularly in the aftermath of the oil fires of Kuwait, everyone is aware of the dangers of pollution.

The heart of Dubai: modern buildings along the creekside.

Leaving more than footprints: near Margham cars put the desert's regenerative powers to the test.

But the greatest impact comes from sustained industrial activity — and here, the lack of any history of heavy industry means that pollution problems have been largely avoided.

Great efforts are being taken to restrict marine contamination from the tankers that travel up and down just off the coastline. Most bathers will agree that there are sometimes small-scale problems with oil and tar washed onto the beaches.

But all the studies that have been carried out so far suggest that there has been no serious pollution of the coastal waters. Officials even offer to swim in the various creeks to prove how clean they are.

There are unsavoury traces of mankind scattered around, of course: bottles, plastic bags, and scattered rubbish line some of the main roads, and piles of rusty tin cans and broken bottles may mark some of the favourite picnic spots in the wadis or by the sea.

But these, unsightly as they are, are superficial blemishes on the landscape. The desert has almost infinite regenerative powers: whatever you do to it, it always comes back in the end.

Greens and fairways

It was said years ago that there can be few better ways of serving humanity than making two blades of grass grow where only one grew before. Walking round the Emirates Golf Club, which must be one of the most impressive examples of the greening of the desert anywhere in the Gulf, we were struck by the enormity of the achievement. Where gently rolling sand dunes and salt flats once shimmered and shifted under the sun, today there is something like 700,000 square metres of undulating grassland. In the spaces between the carefully planted fairways, the plants that once struggled to survive in the desert are now taking advantage of the irrigation, the shelter and the stability of the environment to colonise the spare ground.

The way this operation was carried out, from the first ravaging of the sand by the giant earthmovers to the painstaking planting of the grass, stolon by stolon, is a fascinating example of the interaction of man with an unsympathetic environment. If the people who chip divots out of the

fairways as they hack their way round are slightly less skilled than the engineers who designed the whole thing — that, as they say, is par for the course.

The instructions to the designers, the American company Karl Litten Overseas, were to give the course its unique character by keeping as much desert land as possible, and most of the layout follows the natural contours of the land. But two massive lakes were scooped out of the desert, holding a total of some ten million gallons of water between them, sealed against the salty water-table, and fed from the fresh water pumped out as a by-product from the Dubai Aluminium Company. Without that water supply, the whole project would have collapsed: there is an average of 600,000 gallons pumped onto the course every night of the year.

Choosing what grass to use was a lengthy job in itself: Karl Litten had drawn on his experience in building similar courses in the southern states of the USA to bring in heat-resistant strains, but Gulf Landscape Services, the Dubai company who actually planted the grass, had to test each one in the special desert environment of Dubai. One, which was too slow-

growing, formed minute sand dunes around each stolon of grass as the winds blew in across the desert, until each newly planted area was once again covered in sand. The only sign of the grass beneath was a slight ripple on the surface.

Even the grasses which were eventually chosen, breeds called Tifway and Tifgreen, which had been used on other landscaping projects around the houses and palaces of the Emirates, frequently needed a gentle brushing to clear away the sand after a shamal.

"If forty maids with forty mops
Swept it for half a year,
Do you suppose, the Walrus said,
That they could get it clear...?"

That was Lewis Carroll's question — in this case, they had a few hours at best in which to give the newly planted fairways a chance, but on the other hand, they often had a hundred men working shoulder to shoulder on the job.

There can be few more thankless tasks than trying to sweep away the deserts of Arabia with a brush — but one of them, presumably, is cooling the desert winds with a hosepipe. That was the next problem.

Even several years on, with the grass well established and thriving so well on the heat that it needs mowing twice a day in the summer, the hot, dry winds still create problems. Just blowing across the tiny patches of sand that make up the course bunkers, they often pick up so much heat in the summer that they scorch and kill the grass on the lee side of the bunker. Golf club workers stand out in the summer sun with hoses, spraying the grass to cool it down and keep it alive.

Those, of course, are emergency measures. The golf course's irrigation system has hidden sprinklers no more than 30 metres apart, capable of giving the whole area a double dousing of sweet water as soon as they are switched on.

But, although the effect of the whole programme on the desert environment has been colossal, keeping the desert back is a constant fight. "What would happen," we asked one of the experts from Gulf Landscape Services, "if the Golf Club simply stopped their maintenance work?"

"It would return to the desert," he said, in the precise, matter-of-fact tone of a professional discussing the total destruction of his creation.

"In winter, it might stay green for a week,

Emirates Golf Club.

but after a fortnight, it would look like hay. And in three or four weeks, the fairways would simply be breaking up. The trees might stay a little longer, but the desert shrubs that have grown thicker and bushier would very quickly get thin and straggly again. They might hang on for a few weeks.

"But if it was in May, the whole process would be finished within a couple of months at the very outside. It would have gone back to the desert, and there'd be practically nothing left."

The waters of the ornamental lakes on the course — their beds, unlike those of the irrigation lakes, not sealed against the natural water-table — provide an image of the way the inhospitable desert environment is constantly ready to take over again. Slice or hook a drive into them, and the ball will hit the water with a satisfying splash before sinking out of sight — that is the classic reminder to a golfer not to lift his head as he plays his shot. There's more to it than that here, though. In fact, the balls that land in these lakes don't entirely vanish.

About a metre below the surface, they will suddenly stop sinking, and hang suspended in

Above: Sprinkler systems are designed to make the best use of the precious water.
Below: Jumairah Beach Park.

A second venue for international golf in Dubai: the Creek Golf Course under construction.

One of Jumairah's private gardens.

Gardens in the desert

the middle of the lake. They have sunk through the relatively salt-free water which has drained straight off the surface of the ground, and they are floating on top of the natural water-table. That, being very salty indeed, supports the balls more effectively than the fresh water.

The water used for irrigation, which runs straight off the greens and fairways into the lake, forms a layer like a lens on top of the salty water-table. Fervent gardening and the watering of plants in Jumairah and other residential areas of Dubai, in fact, has produced much the same phenomenon: but it's here at the Golf Club that it's seen to its best effect.

The saline solution, of course, will support much less life than the pure fresh water that is pumped onto the golf course and poured onto the garden. As more and more irrigation is carried out, so more and more fresh water filters through. As the water-table slowly rises, the natural salty water remains beneath the fresh water lens. It sits there as a silent reminder that the desert may retreat for a while — but it never goes away.

It presents the same problems in building the lush parks and private gardens around the Emirates as it gave the designers of the golf course. One of the first jobs is always to carry in tons of salt-free, 'sweet' sand — but even then, plants which may be sensitive to salty water have to be planted on specially-built mounds to keep their roots clear of the natural water-table.

Even with sweet sand and fresh water for irrigation, the Gulf coast is far from being an ideal environment for many ornamental plants. One of the landscape architect's skills is in knowing what plants can be persuaded to grow, and in providing them with the best possible environment.

Salt breezes off the sea can wreak havoc with the most carefully planted trees and bushes — the flame-trees, hibiscus and bougainvillaea: simply position them behind a wall or a bank for shelter, and they will revel in the warmth and the sunshine.

Even after the garden has been planted, it needs constant expert attention to keep it at its best and hold the desert at bay. Yellowing leaves, for instance, might reveal that plants are suffering from a lack of natural iron in the sandy soil-mix: this, and other minerals, are added to give the garden the nutrition it needs.

With skill and hard work, the landscape architects can often impose a foreign order and lushness on an unfriendly landscape. One villa in Dubai, for instance, boasts a whole series of different gardens. One is built in a formal Italian style; there's a cactus garden, precisely constructed Japanese and tropical gardens, and, shimmering unexpectedly in the Arabian sun, a cool, refreshing water-garden. All of them hide behind the same perimeter wall, not 10 minutes from the centre of town.

They all rely on the manipulation of the landscape, and the constant application of minerals, plant foods, and fresh water — and all of them, without constant attention, would crumble back to sand and scrub within a few short summer months.

Elsewhere, landscape architects have often been anxious to preserve the spirit of the natural location, just as the Emirates Golf Club was designed to incorporate as much desert land as possible.

Work on Jumairah's Beach Park started with the careful working out of what would have been the natural shape of the sand dunes which once lined the Gulf coast. It was only when they had reconstructed the original lie of the land with earthmovers and bulldozers that the landscape architects turned to the problems of helping grasses and plants to grow in an inhospitable environment.

Elsewhere, an existing date-palm farm near Al Ain has been transformed into a linked series of features making up a desert garden.

The idea in this project was to reflect the natural appearance of water in a desert environment: the water tumbles down over natural local boulders in a waterfall like the ones found high in the mountains, and then makes its way along a stony wadi bed, to be gathered into the falaj system at the end of it.

From there it is channelled to date palms and fruit trees, much as it has been done by villagers in the Emirates for generations. Wadi cobbles and boulders, palm trees and traditional barasti

Date plantation transformed into a garden.

Agriculture at Siji.

fencing, have all been brought into the site to give it an authentic feel.

Original features remain: the garden is built around falajes that have run with irrigation water for years, and many of the trees and mud walls were on the site from the beginning. But the concept of a desert garden, created to echo a centuries-old tradition, is the work of landscape architects who have brought out and devloped the spirit of an ancient Arab settlement.

But greening the desert has far wider implications than simply enabling people to build gardens or play golf. At various places around the Emirates, a developing agriculture industry is changing the face of what used to be harsh and infertile country.

Food from the desert

As the nomad relied on his camel, so the farmers who gathered around the oases built their lives around their date plantations. Their date palms produced highly nutritious food that could easily be stored, and timber for building. In their shade, other plants could grow — melons, onions, tomatoes, beans and carrots.

It would be a presumptuous man who tried to teach one of those hardy growers about living in harmony with his unforgiving environment: but agriculture today is a highly technical and scientific business.

Something like 40,000 hectares are cultivated, much of it concentrated in the areas of Ras Al Khaimah, Fujairah, and Al Ain. The first two enjoy the benefits of a certain amount of fertile alluvial soil, and occasional rainfall from the mountains, while Al Ain's dairy and grain farms are founded largely on the fertility of the oasis. Where once there was desert, there are now dairy farms, wide expanses of vegetable fields, and productive fruit plots. 'Emirates Strawberries' are exported all over the world.

It is only modern technology — irrigation, fertilisers and pesticides — that has enabled

89

Ploughing the Liwa dunes for farming.

the farmers to transform the desert in this way. And that, sadly, is the problem.

The fear is that over-use of fertilisers and other chemicals could eventually poison the land and destroy the agriculture they are supposed to promote. Government ministers have been trying to persuade farmers that, certainly where soil additives and pesticides are concerned, more doesn't necessarily mean better. The search for big increases in crop yields now could lead to disaster in the future.

Cheap manures and fertilisers are sometimes imported without either information about their ingredients or instructions for their use. Some foreign companies sell pesticides abroad which have already been banned at home as unsafe.

There are dangers, too, in over-using the natural supplies of fresh water. In areas where there is no desalination plant to fall back on, over-pumping the water-table can lead to water failure, abandoned farms, and the return of the desert into what used to be cultivated fields.

These, though, are the problems of any developing agricultural industry. The Emirates are already something like half-way towards being self-sufficient in fruit and vegetables, and there are even seasonal exports to other countries in the region.

With the huge investment that has already gone into irrigation systems, many experts believe that agriculture can only continue to expand, relying on the constant sunshine, which could produce two or even three harvests a year.

It is one factor that is almost certain to continue to change the face of the landscape throughout the Gulf region.

Land from the sea

Engineers have done more in the Gulf than turn the desert green, though. Along the shoreline, around the mouths of the creeks, they have been reclaiming valuable land from the sea, by using the movement of the tides and the winds that used to threaten the seafarers.

It's more than 30 years since the first project started at the mouth of Dubai Creek, with the building of a steel wall out into the sea. The wall stood about a metre above the level of the sea, and its purpose was simply to stop the drifting of sand along the shore that was forming sand bars across the mouth of the creek.

In fact, as the sand built up against the wall,

Fields at Wadi Shwaib.

it formed a new spit of land jutting out into the Gulf. Today, under the cranes and buildings of Port Rashid, it's unrecognisable as reclaimed land, but it marks the start of one of Arabia's most imaginative reclamation projects.

The next stage of the project was a second wall, built out from Deira on the other side of the creek mouth, with the aim of narrowing the entrance to the creek, so as to increase the pressure of the water forced in and out by the tides. The idea was to increase the force with which the sea would scour out the sand, and also to provide a single, constant, navigation channel.

Behind that wall, though, was the perfect site for another land reclamation scheme. Unwanted sand dredged out to create Port Rashid to the south of the creek was piped across and used to fill in the angle between the wall and the existing shoreline. Protected from the tides and currents, the land gradually grew out of the sea: Dubai was producing prime city centre building land almost literally out of nowhere. The operation was more than self-financing: it produced a large profit in the years before oil money started to flow, and it's now provided the land where the Hyatt Regency Hotel and the markets stand.

Reclamation of land, though, was only a by-product of the central scheme. Before the work was started, the depth of the creek was often less than half-a-metre at low tide. Adventurous types who weren't too worried about the state of their footwear could sometimes walk from one side to the other.

Guiding the currents

Narrowing the channel to the sea increased the scouring force of the tides, but the creek also had to be dredged to increase the amount of water in it. The sand, of course, was piped into the reclamation scheme — and today, Dubai Creek is left around six metres deep, and up to some 300 metres across, clear down to its sandstone bottom. The two spits of reclaimed land at the entrance guide the currents and the sand they carry away from the mouth, leaving the creek clear of sediment, without the need for more dredging operations that would disrupt the hectic waterfront business.

Skilful engineering has modified the landscape and created new land at the heart of the city — and done it, incidentally, in a way that has paid for itself many times over.

Trading dhows at Dubai Creek.

Currents around the Creek mouth in the early days of Dubai.

OIL: THE WEALTH OF ARABIA

The Gulf region has known centuries of relative prosperity as a trading route between East and West — but the foundations of today's new wealth were laid down well over a hundred million years ago, under a warm sea.

Countless shellfish, sea urchins, tiny corals, plants and marine animals lived, died and sank gently to the sea bed, mingling with the fine-grained sands and sediments.

But in the shallower waters around the off-shore basin, a reef was forming from the remains of other molluscs and marine creatures — the same primitive creatures whose death masks are so avidly collected at Fossil Valley.

As the water levels slowly fell, the reef gradually spread into what had been the depths of the sea, covering the area with a layer of highly porous rock. Trapped beneath it was the raw material of what was to become Dubai's Khatiyah formation: the oil that was eventually to be discovered and pumped from the Fateh Field.

The whole process took place to a beat only slightly faster than that to which the continent itself was shifting its position. The seas rose and fell, and for ninety or a hundred million years, successive layers of limestone and impervious shales were deposited on top of the organic remains of the life-forms of past millennia.

All the time, bacteria were working on them. Then, intense pressure was generated as the newer, younger rocks were laid down above. With the pressure came searing heat until the three factors of bacteria, pressure and heat worked to convert what had been left behind by plant and animal life into hydrocarbons.

Pipeline from Margham Field, near Dubai.

Uplifted rock structures at Jebel Sumani.

The rock structures and the shifting of the earth were working together as a gigantic geological pressure cooker, turning organic remains into oil and hydrocarbons.

Under pressure, the droplets of oil were forced into the pores of the rock above them, squeezed upwards until they met the barrier of the impermeable layer of shale. The oil that would bring unimagined riches to the Gulf was trapped beneath the surface, waiting through the millions of years to be discovered.

Even older, and hence even deeper, than the oil-bearing rock, though, is the layer of salt that goes back some 500 million years, to a time when only algae, bacteria, sponges and simple life-forms inhabited the earth. Apart from them, it was a dead planet. The salt, too, was squeezed by the increasing pressure over thousands of centuries, and forced upwards into faults and weaknesses in the rocks above it, pushing the layers into dome-like uplifts or anticlines.

In the rock were water and tiny droplets of oil — but the oil, lighter than the water, collected beneath the summit of the dome formed by the impervious cap rock, as if in a trap.

That was one example, the Mishrif formation: similar processes went on, separated by millions of years, in different rock strata around the region. Dubai's offshore Fateh Field alone draws on three separate formations: the Mishrif formation is sandwiched between the Thamama below and the more recent Ilam in the rocks above. A word like 'recent', incidentally, may slip easily off the geologist's tongue: in this case, it means something like seventy-five million years old.

Clues to the riches lying beneath the surface were all over the peninsula for the oil men of the 20th century to find. Sometimes, the upward pressure of the salt formed humps on the surface, as it did at Jebel Ali. Sometimes, the salt itself would find a way though to the surface: the oil, too, might seep out forming stagnant black pools of bitumen.

Occasionally, as in the Margham Field, it was the squeezing of shifting plates of rock, buried beneath the desert sand, which created the anticlines, rather than salt deposits under pressure.

But the principle remained the same: organic remains in a layer of porous rock which would act as the reservoir, topped by an impervious cap-rock which held the oil in place.

Elsewhere in the book, we talk about the stunning beauty of Jebel Hafit as it rears up over the desert near Al Ain. For the first geologists to visit the region, though, Jebel Hafit was more than a tourist attraction: it was an encouraging pointer to the oil wealth that might lie beneath.

Most of the rock structure of the peninsula is hidden beneath the sands, visible only to scientists with seismic equipment. Early surveyors traced the subterranean rock formations by setting off explosions and charting the vibrations that they caused.

But here and there an anticline would show itself on the surface — sometimes worn and eroded over the centuries like Jebel Hafit, but sometimes presenting a clear dome structure, reflecting the pressures on the rock strata far below.

Offshore, several islands in the Gulf show that the same process has been going on under the sea, with either salt uplifts or shifting plates of rock forcing the strata up into dome shapes. The presence of the anticlines showed at least that there would be reservoirs under the surface in which oil could gather. It took several years to find it — in Dubai, for instance, exploration work was going on sporadically during the 40s and 50s, but it was not until June 6, 1966 that the first oil was found, 100 kilometres offshore.

For decades, though, they had known that there was, at the very least, an excellent chance of finding oil. Over the Gulf in Iran, production had started before the First World War; there were the occasional seepages of black, sticky oil on the surface; there were even occasional natural gas fires, blazing like beacons for the surveyors, where gas had leaked through the surface and been ignited.

And all over the region, of course, there were the tell-tale rock formations and the patterns of domes and anticlines to suggest that any oil underground could have been trapped in significant quantities.

But it's unlikely that anyone realised the sheer scale of the discoveries that were to be made. The Gulf contains more than half of the world's proven reserves of crude, and about 25 per cent of its natural gas.

And, just as significant, the hydrocarbons of the Gulf are relatively easy to recover. Oil and gas, of course, do not gather underground in massive reservoirs, waiting conveniently for the oil companies to pump them out like a highly profitable petrol station. Instead, they lie trapped in the spaces of porous sedimentary rock, like water in a sponge. The bigger and better-connected the pores, the more oil will be stored there, the more easily it will flow inside the rock, and the simpler it will be to pump it to the surface.

Around the Gulf, the geological remains of the molluscs of millions of years ago, in which the oil

Gulf oil workers.

lies, are particularly porous. The oil-bearing rocks may lie 2,500 metres or more below the surface, but reaching the oil in significant quantities is today a relatively cheap and simple process.

But there were plenty of problems for the first oil men in the region. Much of the early surveying was done by night, by the light of the moon, because the baking daytime sun made the delicate metal instruments expand and distort. The sea was often too shallow for ships to land with supplies and equipment. Most of the surveying teams had to learn the niceties of desert driving as they went, paying for their inevitable mistakes with long hours wielding a shovel.

Creating a landscape

Now, though, the oil companies have not only come to terms with the natural difficulties of working in a desert environment: they have started manipulating the landscape itself to suit their own requirements.

Over the last decade and a half, they have built artificial islands offshore, scooping away the sea bed to clear deep water channels for supply vessels and tankers, and piling the sand up to provide a base at sea for drilling rigs and other installations. Two of the first such islands were created off Abu Dhabi in 1982, one 12 kilometres offshore at Zubbaya, and the other further out in the Gulf at Hail.

Even the offshore fields are in calm and shallow waters, particularly when compared with the stormy, inhospitable seas from which Britain's North Sea oil is taken.

But it is difficult to exaggerate the effect the oil companies' work has had on a region almost devoid of other natural wealth.

Traditionalists may regret what has happened. Thesiger, before he became reconciled with the modern advances of the region, spoke bitterly of 'an Arabian Nightmare, the final disillusionment'. But the people of the Gulf and beyond have voted in the most convincing way they could — by flooding into what was a harsh and empty land.

In 1946, for instance, when the first oil men arrived on Abu Dhabi island, there were some 2,000 people living there, with many of them spending much of the year in the date gardens of Al Ain. The journey from Dubai, whether by car or camel, was one to daunt the most fearless western explorer. Today, the UAE capital is a prosperous city of a quarter of a million or more — and if the journey down the

Sharjah — another oil platform moves out into the Gulf.

Abu Dhabi road from Dubai is daunting, it's only because of the speed of the cars and the occasional flamboyance of the driving.

Good fortune

Since the first discovery in the southern Gulf in the 30s — Bahrain, in 1932, was the first of the Gulf states to make a positive strike — the wealth of oil has transformed the lives of the people of the region.

Before the oil was found, recession in the West and the development of cultured pearls in the East, had conspired to destroy the pearling fleets of the Gulf within a couple of seasons. The region faced economic disaster.

The first exploration came as the last pearling boats were starting to rot away — and it rescued the region from the threat and the reality of poverty. HH Sheikh Rashid bin Saeed Al Maktoum (the late ruler of Dubai) himself, with a characteristic sardonic realism, named Dubai's first offshore oil-field. He called it Fateh — 'golden opportunity'. That, indeed, is what it has turned out to be.

Dubai's Fateh Field.

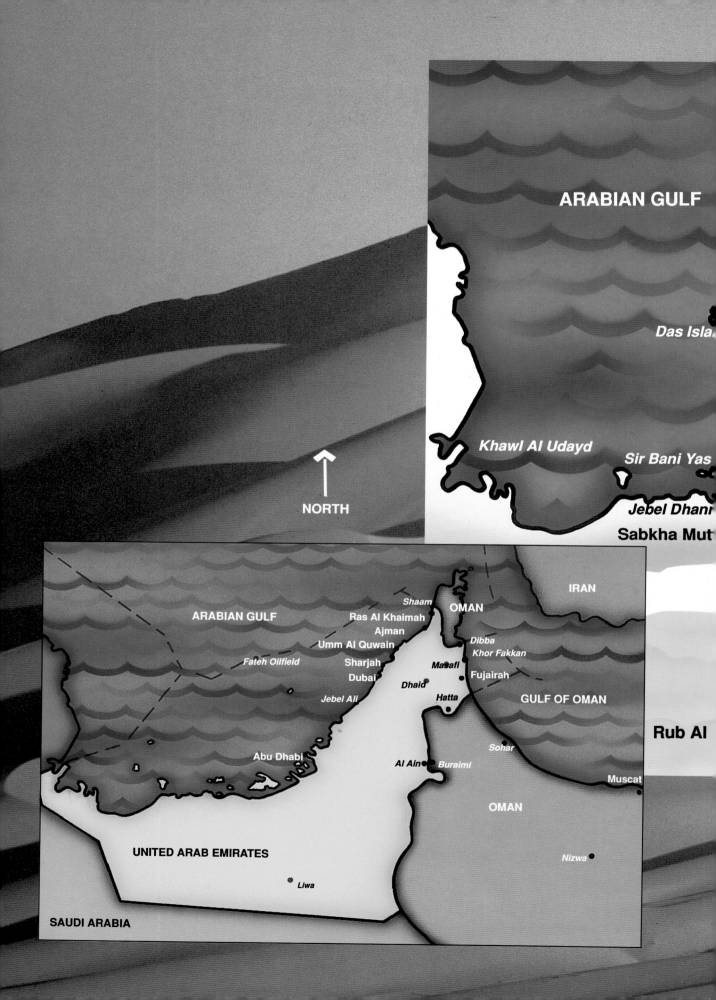

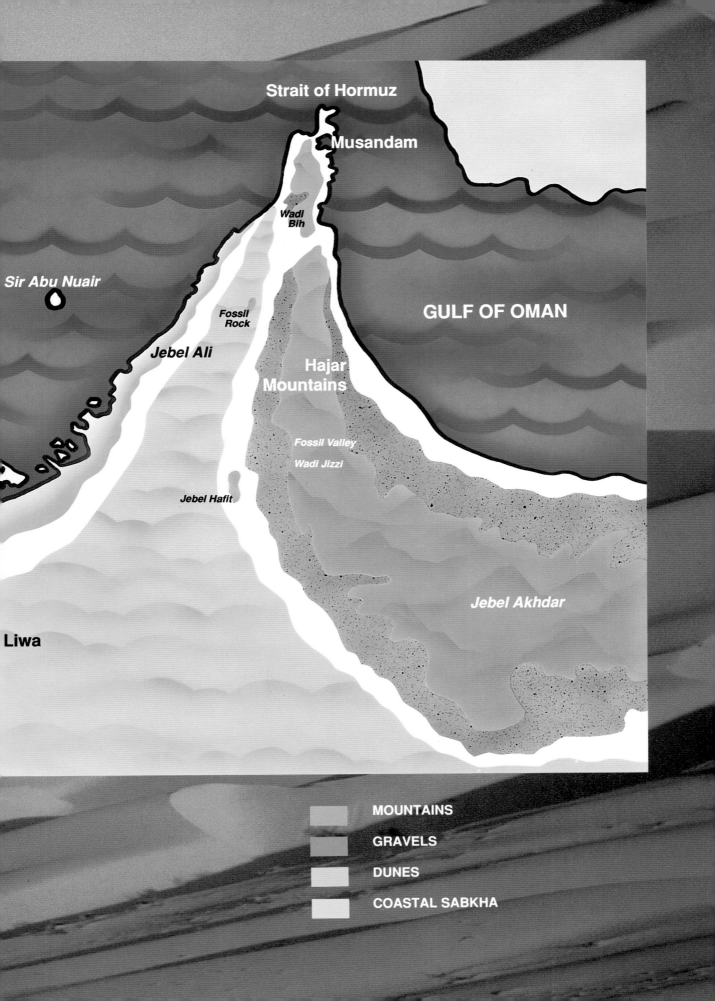

ACKNOWLEDGEMENTS

Many people have helped us with their time, their knowledge and their advice. Among them are Neville Allen, OBE, of Emirates Development International; Dr Fawzi Asadi of Al Ain University's Department of Geography; George Atkinson of Gulf Landscape Services; Steve Davenport of Ocean Routes and Dubai Television; Brian Eccleston of the Qatar Natural History Group; Ian Fetterley and Roy Nurmi of Schlumberger Technical Services; Sergio Magnaldi of the Hatta Fort Hotel; Capt. William Nelson of the Marine Division of Dubai's Department of Ports and Customs; Saud bin Khalid Al Qasimi of the Sharjah Ports and Customs Department; Allen Thyssen of Dubai Petroleum Company and our good friend, Tony Woodward.

Finally, we would like to thank Gulf Landscape Services, whose sponsorship has made possible the publication of this book.

Gulf Landscape Services

BIBLIOGRAPHY

Peter Beaumont et al: *The Middle East, A Geographical Study*, 1988

Z R Beydoun: *Regional Geology and Petroleum Resources*, 1987

Robert Bowen and Ulrich Jux: *Afro-Arabian Geology, A Kinematic View*, 1987

W Donald Davison Jr: *Majlis Al Jinn Cave, Sultanate of Oman*, 1985

Erhard Gabriel (ed): *The Dubai Handbook*, 1986

Andrew Goudie and Andrew Watson (eds): *Desert Geomorphology*, 1980

Andrew Goudie and A Wilkinson: *The Warm Desert Environment*, 1977

Franke Heard-Bey: *From Trucial States to United Arab Emirates*, 1982

Donald A Holm: *Desert Geomorphology in the Arabian Peninsula*, 1960 ('Science' magazine)

St John Philby: *The Empty Quarter*, 1933

Tim Severin: *The Sindbad Voyage*, 1982

Wilfred Thesiger: *Arabian Sands*, 1959

David Thomas (ed): *Arid Zone Geomorphology*, 1989

AUTHORS

Elizabeth Collas and Andrew Taylor have lived in Dubai since 1988.

Elizabeth, the geographer of the family, specialised in desert geomorphology at Oxford University, and since graduating has taught geography in several schools.

Andrew, a writer and journalist who has worked for the Daily Express and BBC Television News, is now a reporter and news editor at Dubai Television, and has contributed articles about the Gulf to many publications, including the Times, Sunday Telegraph and Spectator.

In this book the authors have combined their respective areas of expertise with their varied knowledge of the Gulf to present a fascinating account of the landscape and the immense forces which have shaped it.

Gulf Landscapes is dedicated to their three children, Sam, Abigail and Rebecca.

PHOTO CREDITS

INDEX

Bold type indicates picture

OTHER ARABIAN HERITAGE TITLES

Arabian Profiles
edited by Ian Fairservice
and Chuck Grieve

Land of the Emirates
by Shirley Kay

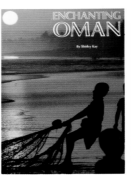

Enchanting Oman
by Shirley Kay

A Day Above Oman
by John Nowell

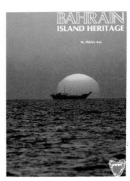

Bahrain-Island Heritage
by Shirley Kay

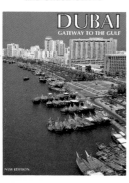

Dubai-Gateway to the Gulf
edited by Ian Fairservice

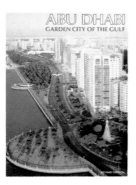

**Abu Dhabi-Garden City
of the Gulf**
edited by Ian Fairservice
and Peter Hellyer

Fujairah-An Arabian Jewel
by Peter Hellyer

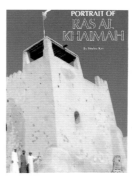

Portrait of Ras Al Khaimah
by Shirley Kay

**Sharjah
Heritage and Progress**
by Shirley Kay

**Architectural
Heritage of the Gulf**
by Shirley Kay
and Dariush Zandi

**Emirates
Archaeological Heritage**
by Shirley Kay

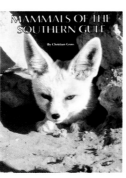

**Mammals
of the Southern Gulf**
by Christian Gross

The Living Desert
by Marycke Jongbloed

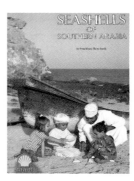

**Seashells
of Southern Arabia**
by Donald and Eloise Bosch

The Living Seas
by Frances Dipper and
Tony Woodward

Sketchbook Arabia
by Margaret Henderson

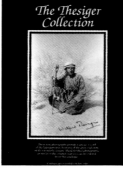

The Thesiger Collection —
a catalogue of unique
photographs by W Thesiger

**Snorkelling
and Diving
in Oman**
by
Rod Salm
and
Robert
Baldwin

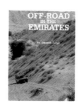

**Off-Road
in the
Emirates**
by
Dariush
Zandi

**Off-Road
in Oman**
by
Heiner K[...]
and
Rebecca
Brickson

**The Green
Guide to
the Emirates**
by
Marycke
Jongbloed